EVERY "THING" YOU'VE EVER DREAMED OF

- **WILD "THINGS"**
- **WONDERFUL "THINGS"**
- **WEIRD "THINGS"**
- **HORRIBLE "THINGS"**
- **FUNNY "THINGS"**
- **NASTY "THINGS"**
- **EXTRAORDINARY "THINGS"**
- **SUPERHUMAN "THINGS"**

An Amazing Exploration of the Living
Monsters and Marvels of Earth

MORE
"THINGS"

by IVAN T. SANDERSON

MORE
"THINGS"

IVAN T. SANDERSON
F.L.S., F.R.G.S., F.Z.S., M.A. (Cantab).

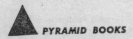

PYRAMID BOOKS • NEW YORK

DEDICATION:

To Marion L. Fawcett, for many years
to us truly ML&F or "Myth, Legend, and
Folklore", but who has done so much
since joining us to pull S.I.T.U.
together and set it on the right road,
paved with efficiency, ditched and
fenced with practicality, and aimed in
the right direction—namely the portals of reality.

MORE "THINGS"

A PYRAMID BOOK

First printing June, 1969

Copyright © 1969 by Ivan T. Sanderson

All Rights Reserved

Printed in the United States of America

PYRAMID BOOKS are published by Pyramid Publications, Inc.
444 Madison Avenue, New York, New York 10022, U.S.A.

ACKNOWLEDGMENTS

"Neodinosaurs" first appeared in *The Saturday Evening Post,* 3 January 1948, under the title "There Could be Dinosaurs"; Copyright © 1948, Curtis Publishing Co.

"Three-Toes—Model A." and "Three-Toes—Model B." first appeared in *Fate* Magazine, December 1967 and January 1968, under the title "That Forgotten Monster—Old Three-Toes"; Copyright © 1967, 1968, Clark Publishing Company.

"Wandering Woodspersons" first appeared in *Argosy* Magazine, February 1968, under the title "First Photos of 'Bigfoot', California's Legendary 'Abominable Snowman'"; Copyright © 1968, Popular Publications, Inc.

"Frozen Mammoths" first appeared in *The Saturday Evening Post,* 16 January 1960, under the title "Riddle of the Frozen Giants"; Copyright © 1960, Curtis Publishing Company.

"Vile Vortices" first appeared in *Argosy* Magazine, August 1968, under the title "The Spreading Mystery of the Bermuda Triangle"; Copyright © 1968, Popular Publications, Inc.

"SSP Versus ESP" first appeared in *The Saturday Evening Post,* 24 October 1943, under the title "The Animals Have It on Us"; Copyright © 1953, Curtis Publishing Company.

"An Hallucination?" first appeared in *Fate* Magazine, October 1965, under the title "Haitian Hallucination—The City That Wasn't There"; Copyright © 1965, Clark Publishing Company.

NOTE: Readers who enjoy a solid examination of a topic before delving into it are invited to turn at once to the Epilogue wherein the author investigates the nature of all "Things" and why they get less than fair or objective treatment from Official Sources. Readers who like their phenomena straight —and exciting—should get on with Chapter one *right away*.

TABLE OF CONTENTS

Part I.—MORE LIVE THINGS

Part II.—MORE MAN THINGS

Part III.—MORE NASTY THINGS

Part IV.—MORE FUNNY THINGS

Part I

MORE LIVE THINGS

Chapter 1.

NEODINOSAURS[1]

THERE HAS BEEN A VERY CURIOUS going-on in Africa for more than a century that needs a good airing. The mere thought of it is an abomination to scientists but it is a matter that never fails to excite our imagination. It revolves around the question—probably for the most part born of wishful thinking—that so many of us asked in our youth; namely, could there be a few dinosaurs still living in some remoter corners of the earth? But first, two expressions of caution.

One is that there actually is not and never has been such a thing as a dinosaur, *per se*, the term being a more general one like "predaceous beasts" than, say "hoofed mammals". It means literally "terrible reptiles" and was initially coined to cover all reptiles discovered as fossils, and at one time it came to include even the larger extinct amphibians and related comparatively tiny creatures only two feet long.[2] There never was any group of animals officially, properly, and scientifically designated that of the *Dinosauria*, although later the term tended to be confined to members of three large groups of terrestrial reptiles that are thought to have become totally extinct some seventy-million years ago. These are now known as the sub-orders *Theropoda*, *Sauropoda*, and *Ornithopoda*. Lately, however, the term has once again swelled to include just about all extinct reptiles and the larger amphibians.[3]

My second word of caution regards the concept of modern-day Africa. Just because it has been so much in the news for the past two decades, has been fought over, and is now allegedly criss-crossed by roads, it does not mean that it is any "lighter" than a century ago. In fact, with the advent of the airplane it has reverted to being the truly dark continent in many respects. Its vast jungles and swamplands have been by-passed in all the modern hubbub, and thousands of locations that were fairly well known fifty years ago have now been virtually lost. The mere size of the place is quite beyond comprehension to those who have not visited it,[4] so it is quite useless to suggest that there is not room in it for all manner of things as yet unknown.

There is really nothing but negative evidence to support the statement that dinosaurs are extinct, while, astonishing as it may seem, there are apparently quite a few people who actually believe that some still do exist. Moreover, the evidence they present, is positive, even though they cannot deny that it is purely circumstantial. Much of it may probably and quite justifiably be disposed of as wishful thinking, as examples of mistaken identity, scientific over-enthusiasm, native stupidity or even bad liquor; but there are some things like the tuatara, a two-foot lizard-shaped creature from New Zealand, and some millions of crocodiles which are just as real as the elephants in our zoos and the cattle in our fields, but which are as old as the oldest dinosaurs. All the facts, moreover, are on record, so let us examine them, beginning with what will probably be regarded as the lunatic fringe.

A well-known South African big-game hunter, delighting in the name of Mr. F. Gobler, returned from a trip to Angola and announced to the Capetown newspaper, the *Cape Argus*,[5] that there was an animal of large dimensions, the description of which could only fit a dinosaur, dwelling in the Djilolo Swamps, and well known to the natives as the "chipekwe". He stated: "Its weight would be about four tons and it attacks rhino, hippo and elephants. Hunters have heard a chipekwe—at night—devouring a dead rhino, crushing the bones and tearing out huge lumps of meat. It has the head and tail of a lizard. A German scientist has photographed it. I went to the swamps in search of it, but the natives told me it was extremely rare, and I could not locate the monster. Nevertheless, I am convinced the chipekwe does exist. Here is the photograph."

This, of course, produced a terrific outburst in the editorial and correspondence columns of the paper, but the astonishing thing is that the majority of the experts, both scientific and sporting, and all with much local knowledge, agreed that it *might* exist. Their reasons will become abundantly clear later.

I doubt if any of us would believe such a tale, even if related in all solemnity by the most renowned explorer. Yet a well-known big-game hunter named Maj. H. C.

Maydon, with over a decade of experience chasing animals in Africa, has written of this and a number of similar statements: "Do I believe them? Of course; why not? I add fifty percent for native exaggeration, but I believe there is more than 'something' in them. I met a man, an old hunter-prospector, once in Livingstone, Rhodesia, who swore that he had seen a water monster in Lake Mweru and had studied its tracks. Why has no one yet seen these beasts in the flesh for certain or brought one to bag? Because they are forest or swamp dwellers. How many people have seen a bongo or a giant forest hog or a yellow-backed duiker, and yet they are not excessively rare."[6]

The greatest animal dealer of all time, Carl Hagenbeck, not only believed in such reports but actually invested a very considerable sum in an expedition which he sent to Africa under his best professional collector to search for the creature. A hard-boiled businessman with many years' experience in buying and selling animals simply does not do such a thing unless he has very real grounds for expecting concrete returns on his money. Hagenbeck had such grounds, which he states in his own words as follows: "I received reports from two quite distinct sources of the existence of an immense and wholly unknown animal said to inhabit the interior of Rhodesia. Almost identical stories reached me, first, through one of my own travelers and, secondly, through an English gentleman who had been shooting big game in Central Africa. The reports were thus quite independent of each other. The natives, it seemed, had told both my informants that in the depths of the great swamps there dwelt a huge monster, half elephant, half dragon. This however, is not the only evidence for the existence of the animal. It is now several decades since Menges, who is, of course, perfectly reliable, heard a precisely similar story from the Negroes; and still more remarkable, on the walls of certain caverns in Central Africa there are to be found actual drawings of this strange creature. From what I have heard of the animal, it seems to me that it can only be some kind of dinosaur, seemingly akin to the *brontosaurus*."[7, 8]

Now it is easy enough to scoff at these tales and even to pity the sporting major and the poor gullible animal-dealer. It is quite permissible to view such reports with a healthy skepticism and it is assuredly prudent to do so.

Nonetheless, to let the matter rest there would be utterly unscientific. The very basis of science is a healthy skepticism—one, moreover, that should question the skeptic who denies the possibility of anything just as readily as it should question the benighted traveler who dares affirm it.

The borderland of zoology is very extensive; the number of animals still to be discovered on this small planet is much greater than is popularly realized or science is prepared to advertise.[9] Nor are all of these microscopic worms or tiny, obscure tropical beetles. There is the famous case of the okapi, an animal as large as a horse that was only a rumor until 1900 but is now well known. The number of entirely new types of animals that are discovered every year is amazing. And this brings us to the next set of facts which anybody with a truly unbiased mind should contemplate.

A notion has somehow gained popular credence that the surface of the earth is now fully explored and for the most part well known and even mapped. There was never a greater misconception. The percentage of the land surface of the earth that is actually inhabited—that is to say, lived upon, enclosed, farmed or regularly traversed—is quite limited. Even if the territory that is penetrated only for hunting or the gathering of food crops be added, vast areas still remain completely unused.[10]

There are such areas in every continent, areas that for years are never even entered by man. Nor are these only the hot deserts of the torrid regions or the cold deserts of the poles. I have visited a house in New Jersey behind which the woods extend in one direction, unbroken by so much as a path, for twenty-one miles.

In parts of the tropics there are areas of quite staggering immensity which no man has as yet been able to penetrate. Whole mountain ranges in Australia have never even been seen from the ground; large parts of the northern Himalayas are as yet unvisited; regions of New Guinea have never been reached, and considerable portions of the Amazon valley are quite unknown. The Addar swamps in Central Africa cover 1800 square miles, those of the Bahr el Ghazal several thousands, and parts of them cannot be traversed. Just because a map is covered with names does not mean that the country is known. Aerial surveys made with modern photographic techniques only add to this popular misconception, for many of the physical features are recorded in some detail then rapidly find their way into our atlases. They are given names and fill up the space, but at the same time the country remains absolutely untouched.

The notion, therefore, that some beast could not exist because of its size or because somebody would sooner or later have seen it, is really quite absurd. There might easily be creatures as big as elephants living in some profusion in, say, the back of the Guyanas, which are now only a few hours' flight in a commercial plane from Miami. Such animals might have been well known to several thousand people for hundreds of years, but their presence would still be unsuspected by us, for few of the Amerindians—who from aerial surveys are known to exist in that area—have ever come out or even been seen by anyone from outside.

Another fact that is often not sufficiently appreciated even by experts is the extraordinary selectivity displayed by many animals in choosing their places of habitat. Larger animals especially tend to stay within a limited area that is often very distinctive as far as vegetation and other environmental conditions are concerned. Nomadic animals often travel only from one patch of some particular kind of forest to another of the same, avoiding all other kinds as they would a forest fire. Hippopotamuses will abound in certain stretches of a river and never be seen in others.

This trait often accounts for the supposed rarity of many animals, when in point of fact—apart from species that are actually on the road to extinction—there is probably no such thing as a rare animal. It is merely a question of finding where it lives and how it lives, and in that place it will prove to be quite common. Any creature living in a tropical swamp surrounded by dry jungles would always stay there and, if that swamp could not be penetrated by man, might never be seen. In such a swamp of two thousand square miles' extent, many very large beasts could lurk.

The possibilities become even greater if the animals in question be semi-aquatic; it is interesting to note in this connection that all the accounts of as-yet-unidentified-beasts which sound like descriptions of dinosaurs are of swamp creatures that retreat into the water when alarmed.

The vastness of Africa is a byword and can be attested to by any who have flown over it, but to be really appreciated it has to be seen from the ground. Also, it is only on the ground that one comes to understand the true nature of the tropical forests and swamplands. A companion and I once spent a full five minutes peering into a small patch of bushes trying to see an animal apparently about as bulky as the two of us put together, that we could actually hear breathing. We never did see it, even when it took fright and left, making about as much noise as a light tank![11] On another occasion I was in a canoe among reeds in Africa and, after looking up at the sun ahead to take my bearings, bent down to pick up a cigarette. When I looked up again there was a full-grown bull elephant almost on top of me. As I watched, quivering with fright, it sank down behind the reeds, and although I immediately stood up in the canoe so that I could almost see over the swamp, I never even heard the huge beast again, nor did I see so much as a single reed move. And this was only a mile from a native village of two thousand souls, in an area where elephants had not, as far as I could learn, been seen within living memory.[12]

Small wonder, then, that residents of Africa, and especially those who have hunted big game in more distant parts, do not readily scoff at these tales which provoke us to so much laughter—tales such as that brought out of the Congo by a certain Monsieur Lepage in 1920.[13]

This man returned from a hunting trip and announced that he had come upon an extraordinary animal of great size in a swamp. It had charged him, making a snorting noise, and he had fired wildly; but seeing that it did not halt, he had retreated precipitately. When the monster abandoned the chase he turned and examined it through a pair of binoculars for a considerable period of time. He stated that it was eight meters—about twenty-six feet—long, had a long pointed snout, a short horn above the nostrils, and a scaly hump on its shoulders. The forefeet appeared to be solid like those of a horse, but the hindfeet were separated into digits.

The most astonishing thing about these reports, however, is not so much their prevalence as the widespread points of their origin. Here again our modern atlases are very misleading because the practice—born quite properly of necessity—of squeezing the whole of Africa onto one page gives the impression that the Cameroons are not really very far from the Upper Nile. This distance is actually 1600 miles, and the territory in between is a vast land of forests, swamps, and savannahs. The natives on one side have no connection whatsoever with those on the other, and yet very similar stories are prevalent at both extremes.

These native tales are heard throughout the equatorial rain-forest belt from Gambia in the west to the Nile in the east, and south to Angola and Rhodesia. Carl Hagenbeck's collectors picked them up in Liberia, and the leader of a German expedition to the Cameroons in 1913 made a very interesting report which has never been published in full, but which has been quoted by several others. In widely separated areas, he collected descriptions of an alleged beast named the "Mokele-mbembe" from experienced native guides who could not possibly have known each other. His description states:

"The animal is said to be of a brownish-gray color with a smooth skin, its size approximating that of an elephant; at least that of a hippopotamus. It is said to have a long and very flexible neck and only one tooth but a very long one; *some say it is a horn.* A few spoke about a long muscular tail like that of an alligator. Canoes coming near it are said to be doomed; the animal is said to attack the vessels at once and to kill the crews, but without eating the bodies. The creature is said to live in the caves that have been washed out by the river in the clay of its shores at sharp bends. It is said to climb the shore even at daytime in search of food; its diet is said to be entirely vegetable. This feature disagrees with a possible explanation as a myth. The preferred plant was shown to me; it is a kind of liana with large white blossoms, with a milky sap and applelike fruits. At the Ssombo River I was shown a path said to have been made by this animal in order to get at its food. The path was fresh and there were plants of the described type near by. But since there were too many tracks of elephants, hippos, and other large mammals, it was impossible to make out a particular spoor with any amount of certainty."[14]

This brings up the whole question of native tales, over

which there is perhaps more acrimonious debate than over any other subject. Opinions appear to be about equally divided among those who have lived in Africa, but both parties tend to overlook certain facts. Because of his animistic beliefs, the African lives in a world peopled by a host of spirits which are nonetheless just as real to him as animals are to us, and he may describe these with great clarity of expression. However, we must at the same time consider the fact of the African's customary and remarkable knowledge of natural history; usually, he not only has a name for all the animals in his country but also knows their habits and their slightest variations in great detail.

The African can, however, develop a maddening habit of exaggeration or even outright fabrication if he desires to please an inquiring foreigner. Against this, in turn, must be placed his very widespread reluctance to publicize anything in his territory that might conceivably be of value to the outsider lest—as he has learned from unhappy experience—a new tax immediately be clapped upon it. If you do get a tribal African's confidence and he starts to talk about animals, as opposed to the spirit creatures of his country, it is well worth while to listen intently, for it must not be forgotten that certain Africans always contended that mosquitoes had something to do with malaria, a fact we proved only quite recently. Similarly, others talked about the okapi for a very long time before it was actually shot by a white man. But sometimes the African's patience with us and our disbelief of things he knows well becomes exhausted, and even he resorts to the writing of official minutes.

I must interject here a brief account of a personal experience that occurred in 1932 when I was with the well-known explorer and animal collector, W. M. (Gerald) Russell, and two young Africans employed by us, Bensun Onun Edet and Bassi Aga of the Anyang people. We had paddled all day up a remarkable river named the Mainyu which ran north, straight as a manmade canal, from a large circular pool in which another small river emptied, and from which the mighty Cross River emerged on its way south between the Cameroons and Nigeria to the Atlantic at Calabar. The Mainyu itself was over a hundred miles long, arising in the Assumbo Mountains to the north, ending in this straight run, then cutting a slightly tortuous gorge through a ridge of limestone four-hundred-feet high that lay athwart its entrance to the Mamfe Pool. All the way it ran through the uninhabited, (by any humans) high, deciduous, Equatorial rain-forest, between smooth rock shelves backed by strands of white sand with lush short herbage, behind which the towering forest rose like a cathedral wall, its foliage overhanging the sandy beach. From the giant trees of this forest wall hung innumerable creepers (locally called lianas) both enormous and fine as cotton threads. Many bore exotic flowers and enormous, globular green fruits, looking like footballs, and just as tough.

On returning downstream to the Mamfe Pool from a day of very hard paddling upstream on a collecting trip, we just glided along, paddling only now and then to maintain way. Sundown was approaching as we entered the gorge. Gerald Russell was in the lead canoe with Bassi; I followed about a hundred feet behind with Bensun. There were deepening shadows in the gorge and all along its towering vertical walls at water-level were the arched tops of huge caves. We had previously penetrated some of these at the pool-end of the gorge to collect a certain kind of very rare frog, but we had never before passed these huge ones farther upstream.

When we were about in the middle of the mile-and-a-half-long winding gorge, the most terrible noise I have heard, short of an on-coming earthquake or the explosion of an aerial-torpedo at close range, suddenly burst from one of the big caves to my right. Ben, who was sitting up-front in our little canoe with a "moving" paddle, immediately dropped backward into the canoe. Bassi in the lead canoe did likewise, but Gerald tried to about-face in the strong swirling current, putting himself broadside to the current. I started to paddle like mad but was swept close to the entrance of the cave from which the noise had come. Thus, both Gerald and I were opposite its mouth; just then came another gargantuan gurgling roar and something enormous rose out of the water, turned it to sherry-colored foam and then, again roaring, plunged below. This "thing" was shiny black and was the *head* of something, shaped like a seal but flattened from above to below. It was about the size of a full-grown hippopotamus—this head, I mean.

We exited from the gorge at a speed that would have done credit to the Harvard Eight and it was not until we entered the pool that Bassi and Ben came-to. What we wanted to know, what was this monster? Neither could enlighten us as they were not river people. However, both finally yelled "M'kuoo-m'bemboo", and grabbed their paddles. When we reached the little beach at the far side of the pool where we kept our canoes, we were met by the rest of our gang, some twenty-strong and all local men. They were very shaken and solicitous of our safety. All the river people among them confirmed Bassi and Ben's diagnosis. These animals lived there all the time, they told us, and that is why there were no crocodiles or hippos in the Mainyu. (There were hundreds of both in the pool, the other river, and the Cross River.) But, they went on, "M'koo" does not eat flesh but only the big liana fruits and the juicy herbage by the river.

Later we moved across that river permanently and camped nearby. We found huge pathways through the herbage from the river and masses of the great, tough, green "footballs" smashed up, and some with pieces, a foot wide, bitten out of them just as we bite a piece out of an apple. But now back to official reports.

The now famous report of the late King Lewanika, of the Barotse tribe, is of this nature. The king, who took great interest in the fauna of his country, constantly heard of a large reptile that lived in the great swamps. He had passed this information on, but, since nobody believed it, he gave strict orders that the next time any of his people saw the animal they were to tell him immediately. After some time three men reported, saying that they had come across the beast at the edge of a marsh, that it had a long neck and small, snakelike head, and that it had retreated into the swamp on its belly. King Lewanika immediately visited the spot and states in his official minutes that it had left a track in the reeds "as large as a full-sized wagon would make were its wheels removed."

Other native evidence comes from widely separated sources. An experienced white hunter named Stephens, who was also in charge of a long section of the telegraph line which runs along the banks of the Upper Nile, has given a great deal of information about a large, swamp-dwelling reptile known to a number of tribes as the "Lau."[15] The natives described the animal to Stephens in great detail and more than one of them affirmed that they had been present at the killing of a "Lau." They variously described it as being between forty and a hundred feet long, but concurred in stating that the body was only about as big as a donkey; that it was dark yellow in color, and that it had a vicious, snakelike head, with large tentacles or wiry hairs with which it reached out to seize its prey. Later, a Belgian administrator from the Congo asserted that he had seen a "lau" several times in a swamp and had shot at it.

The most convincing native account, however, comes from Northern Rhodesia, and is of the animal called the "Chipekwe." An Englishman who spent eighteen years on Lake Bangweulu in that country has given an account of the slaying of one, as described by the local chief, who had it from his grandfather.[16] Apparently the tribesmen killed the creature with hippo spears. It had a smooth, hairless, dark body, and the head was adorned with a single white ivory horn. The story was firmly rooted in local tradition; the Englishman believed in the existence of the animal, for he reports that a retired local administrator had heard some very large animal splashing in a lake in the nighttime and had examined large unknown spoor on the bank the next morning.

The mention of a single ivory horn brings us to a whole set of most interesting facts that were assembled from quite another source. Some years ago during the excavation of the famous Ishtar Gate of Babylon by the German professor, Robert Koldewey, a number of startlingly realistic bas-reliefs of a dragonlike animal with curiously mixed features were brought to light. It had a scaled body, long tail and neck, hindfeet of a bird and forefeet of a lion, and a strange reptilian head sporting a single straight, upright horn like that of a rhinoceros, wrinkles under its neck, a crest like a modern iguana lizard, and a very pronounced, serpentine tongue. At first this fabulous creature was classed along with the winged, human-headed bulls and other fabulous monsters of Babylonian mythology, but profound researches gradually forced the professor to quite a different conclusion.[17]

The creature had the name of the "Sirrush" and the priests were said to have held it in a dark cavern in the temple. It was depicted on the walls of the Ishtar Gate in great numbers and in association with a large, oxlike animal which is now known to have been the extinct aurochs—very definitely a real animal. When analyzed, allowing for considerable Babylonian artistic license, the strangely mixed characters of the "Sirrush" appeared to be much less fabulous than had at first been supposed, and, despite his solid Teutonic background, Professor Koldewey became more and more convinced that it was not a representation of a mythical creature but an attempt to depict a real animal, an example of which had actually been kept alive in Babylon in very early days by the priests. After much searching in the depths of his cautious scientific soul, he even made so bold as to state in print that this animal was one of the plant-eating, bird-footed dinosaurs, many types of which had by that time been reconstructed from fossil remains. He further pointed out that such remains were not to be found anywhere in or near Mesopotamia and that the "Sirrush" could not be a Babylonian attempt to reconstruct the animal from fossils. Its characters, as shown in Babylonian art from the earliest times, had not changed, and they displayed great detail in scales, horns, wrinkles, the crest and the serpentine tongue, which, taken together, could not all have been just thought up after viewing a fossilized skeleton.

On further analysis, the "Sirrush" seems to display characteristics of the "Chipekwe" of Lake Bangweulu and of Monsieur Lepage's beast from the Congo. The single horn on the snout, the scaled hump on the shoulders, the solid forefeet and cloven hindfeet, the long neck and small serpentine head and even the "tentacles" of the "Lau" all appear in the "Sirrush." But, much more significant is the little matter of a certain dinosaur of the *Theropod* or so-called "beast-footed" group known as *Ceratosaurus* or the "reptile with a horn". This had a single, upright, white horn on its snout, was probably scaled at least in part, had rather long kangaroo-like hind legs with only three toes like a bird. This is rather annoying because the designation thero-pod means beast or mammal-like-footed, while another of the dinosaurian groups is called ornitho-pod which means bird-footed and its members have three, four, or even five toes! The *theropods* were carnivorous, and this would coincide with the hippo-eating proclivities of the "Chipekwe." We have no evidence from fossils that *Ceratosaurus* was scaled but there is no reason why it should not have been; also, if you look at the head of a large, old iguana in profile you will note just such features as the "Sirrush" displays, namely, gular or throat folds of skin, a crest rising to a point on the crown of the head and then running down the neck and along the back, a very round prominent eye, a slim lower jaw with prominent scales, and sooner or later you will see the forked tongue flick out. Recently, the way in which the skeletons of many of the dinosaurs have been articulated and set up in museums has been very seriously criticized by a group of palaeontologists. (See bibliography.)[18] They contend that the ancient large reptiles were erected upon (like mammals), rather than slung between, the limbs (like lizards). It is possible therefore that dinosaurs like *Ceratosaurus*, despite its small front limbs, spent much time like a browsing kangaroo with its forefeet on the ground, and since the hands had five little clawed fingers it would be rather natural that a Babylonian sculptor should liken them unto a lion.

The only jolt to this theory is that the only one-horned *theropod*—this *Ceratosaurus*—is known only from the Cretaceous period of North America. However, this does not mean that it could not have had an ally in Africa, since there are closely related *theropods* of other kinds known from both continents.

The final link in this chain of evidence may well be the findings of some archaeological digs in Somalia. These brought to light numerous massive structures of a type known only from the Mesopotamian region, composed of baked bricks, some of which were glazed just like those built into the wall and gate of Ishtar. This is much less fabulous than it sounds, for there is absolute evidence that seaborne trade had been carried on by the Sumerians, before the rise of Babylon, between Mesopotamia and the east coast of Africa which was called "Me-lukh-kha" and was said to be inhabited by Salmuti, meaning "black men". If a horned, *theropod* dinosaur existed in Africa at that time, a captive specimen or specimens might well have been shipped back to Mesopotamia, where they would undoubtedly have created quite a stir and become the exclusive property of the ruling priesthood; in fact, the "beast in the pit" of the Bible. Their presence as sacred beasts would prompt the making of very careful portraits of them on important monuments.

Whether the Babylonian "Sirrush" and the other creatures rumored to have come from Africa exist now, or ever existed at all, is a matter that can be proved conclusively only by the discovery of either a live specimen or of fresh bones in association with the remains of men. But if they do exist, the question that immediately springs to mind is, could they be dinosaurs? The answer, perhaps rather surprisingly, is yes.

Neither in its general nor its restricted sense does the name dinosaur necessarily imply primitiveness of structure, great geological age, or even large size, for there are many medium, small, and tiny ones. The crocodiles as a group are just as old and individually much larger than many dinosaurs, while the tortoises belong to one of the most primitive of all reptilian stocks. The little lizard-shaped tuatara which still lives on some islands off New Zealand, is, in the general sense, a dinosaur and it is much more primitive and comes from an older stock than those three groups which we call dinosaurs in the more restricted sense.

This puts the whole matter in an entirely different light. If the tortoises, the tuatara, and the crocodiles have managed to survive from the age of reptiles, there is really no reason why members of the other groups, some much less primitive and including those that we may choose to call dinosaurs, should not also have survived. The majority of the reptiles disappeared at the end of what is called the Cretaceous period, after which the more active and "clever" mammals took over. But there is no reason why some might not have lingered on until today in the vast and isolated swamps of Africa—the one part of the world that has remained tropical and comparatively stable since the Cretaceous period and which was almost entirely unaffected by the great ice ages and the mountain-building disturbances of intervening times.

It is indeed a very curious business that merits our consideration and, in my opinion, some active investigation. Can the whole thing be the product of wishful thinking? Can all these big-game hunters, animal collectors, game wardens, and princely African writers of official minutes be pure sensation seekers or under the influence? Did Professor Koldewey just go daft and throw away his high scientific standing with carefree abandon?

There could be dinosaurs alive today, so let us try to maintain what should be the true scientific spirit and simply say that, as yet, there is no positive evidence that they do still exist.

Chapter 2.

THREE TOES—MODEL A.

AMONG THE MULTIFARIOUS aggravations that mere existence provides to taunt the sincere fortean and notably the zoologically inclined, there is one that truly annoys me. I fully admit that this is a grossly egocentric attitude, but then I was trained primarily as a zoologist, worked professionally in that field for many years, and have spent the rest of my life mixed up in it in one way or another. Then also, this is a matter that I was intimately mixed up in, *per se*, and it is the one item in an otherwise seemingly quite orderly array that just does not fit the pattern. It jolted me in the first place and I still develop something akin to the vibrations every time I am forced to go over it again. But forced I am, and at fairly regular intervals to boot because, like UFOs and other monsters, it just will not go away and keeps cropping up. But first a word of explanation of the term *monster*.

The dictionaries' definition of a monster is rather revealing. The Latin word *monstrosum* originally meant a divine omen, indicating misfortune. Only later was it applied to "animals or plants departing greatly in form or structure from the usual type of the species", and thence to imply also "fabulous or actually existing animals of strange, grotesque, or horrible form". Later still, it came to mean also "any enormous animal or *thing*". Thus, the word today has two rather distinct connotations: one *grotesque*, the other, enormous in *size*. Moreover, as with our classic word *Things*, it has acquired still other meanings, such as "that little monster" (referring to somebody else's child), "a monstrous lie", or even the microscopic "monster that causes syphilis".

Be all this as it may, there remains the specific matter of large animalian monsters of land, sea, ocean, lake, and river which are reported but which have not yet been caught and identified. These have become pretty well patternized, notably through the prolonged, profound, and truly scientific researches of Dr. Bernard Heuvelmans of the Royal Institute of Natural Science of Belgium (see bibliography for his works).[19] By painstakingly eliminating all possible outright hoaxes and lies and cutting out any report that could be a case of mistaken identity, then submitting all the thousands of remaining reports to a computer, this scientist has come up with a very orderly and logical taxonomy of the great as-yet-uncaughts, which in no way, or in any case, violates the precepts of our current understanding of the physiological, anatomical, or morphological patterns of animal life on our planet, past and present. Odd this host of creatures may be, but one and all fit at least closely (if not neatly) into some classificatory slot that we already have open for its reception—except for this wretched one; and this for unique reasons.

First, it seems from the evidence and the descriptions of all the host of creatures analyzed, that they are represented by several of the major types of vertebrated animals—namely, mammals, reptiles, fishes, and possibly amphibians—and in the case of the smaller ones, by certain types of invertebrates such as worms, molluscs, or even arthropods. What is more, those reported on land seem to conform to the known patterns of extant or fossil land-animals; those from swamps conform to known swamp animals, and similarly for river, lake, sea, and ocean forms —except, once again, this bloody item.

This *Thing* is thus a true *Monster*. I have named it "Three-Toes" to avoid getting involved in all manner of abstruse wrangles as to its identity and its own intraclassification as a group, or at least as an apparent type. It constitutes, as I say, the greatest puzzle I have yet encountered, and it needs a damned good airing. So far it has not gotten this and, as I happen to have the details, I am going to take this opportunity of presenting them to you—and, by jingo, *in detail*.

"Three-Toes" have a fairly venerable background but a history in no way comparable to that of other classes of sea-monsters like the "Long-necks." In fact, apart from some odd little wooden statuettes of doubtful provenance from the Indonesian islands of Bali, Lombok, Flores, and Timor, the civilized world does not appear to have been aware of them until about a hundred years ago. There may, I believe, be a simple reason for this. One type of them (Model B., see chapter 3) appears to be southern-hemisphere type, if not sub-antarctic, and only to wander north of the equator on rare occasions, possibly due to very rare and exceptional circumstances. On the other hand, they may truly be only a "class" of creatures erroneously grouped together because of a certain basic similarity in the structure of their feet; because this particular feature of their structure is the only one we know much about. In fact, this may be a case paralleling that of the original Abominable Snowman. Any and all humanoid foot imprints, forming bipedal tracks, were dubbed those of this Himalayan monstrosity because, in my opinion, not even professional monster-hunters could at first stomach the suggestion that there might be half a dozen "unknowns" involved. There may be at least *three* quite distinct kinds of animals of large size, living in salt water, and having three-toed feet—and only two feet, at that.

Prior to 1937, Three-Toes had left tracks on several widely dispersed beaches throughout the world—southern New Zealand, Tasmania, Queensland, Patagonia, and, of all places, Nantucket Island. Then there was the extraordinary business of Kerguelen Island (but more of this anon). In all of these cases there was nothing more observed than three-toed imprints forming bipedal tracks in the sand or mud. These came out of the sea, wandered about on the beach, and then went back into the sea. They were only remarked upon because of their enormous size—when measurements were given, they were always in the nature of eighteen inches in length for the prints, with a stride of about six feet—their local novelty, and the rather vague feeling that there was no known animal of that size that had such feet. However, these early reports are all delightfully vague, quite apart from being treated facetiously. But then, in those days, the attitude toward monsters was quite different to that of today. The general public, especially in outlandish places, knew nothing of zoology and still lived in the mediaeval world of the bestiaries in which all manner of monsters like unicorns and sea-serpents were quite acceptable. The savants, on the other hand, were a hundred per cent skeptical of anything that they had not already got in their limited collections.

They were still skeptical in 1937 when a Mr. Aleko Lilius applied to the Department of Zoology of the University of the Witwatersrand, at Johannesburg, South Africa, for help in identifying the maker of a series of three-toed tracks and the depositor of a large pile of droppings containing fish remains, on a beach in Natal near the Mozambique border in South Africa. The famous coelacanth fish, *Latimeria,* had not yet turned up off that same coast so that poor Mr. Lilius ran into a completely blank wall. When I enquired into the matter ten years later, the droppings had been "forgotten" and the scientist who had been contacted by Mr. Lilius refused to comment on the photographs, though he admitted having seen them.[20] What happened was this:

Aleko Lilius had repeatedly heard from Zulus, Tongas, and Shangaans native to this area about a creature they called the *Silwane manzi* which they said came out of the sea. He obtained some very convincing first-hand descriptions of the beast from several Zulus who said they had seen them. They said these animals were covered with scales like those of a crocodile but that they were nothing like crocodiles, were much larger, and had heads like huge turtles. No native claimed to know of one ever being captured or killed, nor had skeletons ever been found, but their three-toed foot tracks were common and their droppings were considered to be extremely powerful *muti* or medicine—so valuable indeed that one witchdoctor who tried to imitate or "manufacture" it, had been caught and killed for his pains. Lilius went to the coast and set up camp at a place where the 'Mkuzi and Umfolozi Rivers debouch into the Indian Ocean, an area of sand dunes covered with thick scrub, endless white sand beaches, and many large shallow brackish lagoons to landward.[21]

There he was visited by a game warden who informed him that a retired banker by the name of G. F. Timbrell, who had a summer camp up the estuary, had a few months previously observed a pair of large dragon-like animals walk up the beach on their hind legs. He stalked them with a camera but they became alarmed and dashed back into the sea. Lilius was much impressed by the fact that the game warden accepted the facts reported by both this white man and the local natives. However, while the warden was present the natives clammed up, probably, as he says, because they felt the beast might be classed as royal game, the killing or molestation of which carried very dire penalties. After the warden had gone, however, they opened up again, and shortly afterwards they came in to report fresh tracks some miles up the coast. Unfortunately a heavy rain and wind obliterated these by the time Lilius got there.

Shortly afterward the mountain came to Muhammed, as it were, in the form of the monster itself to Lilius. As he told me the story in an interview, he was about to turn in one night rather late when his small dog became greatly disturbed and, on going out of the tent, he had heard some large animal moving about in the thick bush. He stalked the animal with a flashlight and saw a pair of rather small green eyes at some height from the ground. The owner of these eyes took off toward the sea, making a great rumpus. Following as fast as he could, Lilius came upon huge three-toed tracks leading down to the surf. The creature had snorted near the camp and when it rushed into the sea it "made a splash (that) sounded like a ton of bricks" Lilius said.

Not having flashbulbs he could not get any photos of these tracks and during the night a strong wind blew up and obliterated them. Bad weather continued for four days and then came a sudden oppressive lull. Once again Lilius was about to turn in late when the same snorting started up near the camp. Going in pursuit he heard the animal crashing ahead but the thick bush and soft sand almost brought Lilius to a stop, and again the animal made it into the surf, again leaving a set of tracks, and again a wind sprang up before morning and obliterated them. The next day the wind dropped and he went up the beach to fish. He noticed two vultures squabbling over something in the sand dunes and went to investigate and stumbled on masses of the footprints. Dashing back to camp for his camera he called one of his native servants. They then returned to the tracks and took a remarkable series of photographs.

These tracks, Aleko Lilius told me, seemed to indicate that the creature had hopped up the banks on its two hind legs, but that in other places, there were much smaller tracks in between them as if of forefeet, and also long slash-like marks intermittently between these, along the central line of travel, which he presumed were of a tail held high and only touching the ground every now and then. Following these backward down to the beach he then came upon a considerable pile of large faeces which contained fish bones.

The toes were all clawed. Careful measurement showed

the right foot to be a trifle smaller than the left. It measured an average of 16″ from the middle claw-tip to the back of the heel and was thirteen inches wide where the toes joined the foot. The left one averaged out at 16¼ x 13½″. The distance between the toe-tips from the-outside-in was 9″ and 6¾″. The stride, which is to say the distance between the toe-tip of one imprint on one side (say, the right foot) to the back of the heel of the next imprint was 49″. The toes dug into upgrades, and no heel impression appeared.

This was Mr. Lilius' story and I have a set of very clear photographs to prove it. The prints are there, showing a stride that is not normally matched even by a tall man running, accompanied by the tail marks and the little intermediate handlike tracks on level places, but no signs of human or other tracks anywhere about. Mr. Lilius gave me a copy of an article he had had published in a leading national magazine in 1944 which gave a lot more to the story,[22] ending up with an account of his catching a local witchdoctor making similar tracks with a wooden instrument. Yet, in this extended account appears a long shot of the alleged beast itself in the Umfolozi lagoon which he describes as looking like a huge weasel with two small sharp ears or horns. Further, he records a gruesome tale of murder by said witchdoctor and the finding of parts of a dismembered human corpse along a trail of the three-toed tracks. However, two caches of human entrails were found farther on, where there were no tracks, partly buried in the sand, and when Lilius climbed a tree by the lagoon shore to try for a shot at the monster which his native helpers had spotted, the torso of a human corpse milled up from the roil caused by said monster surfacing.

All of this lends an air of doubt and mystery to the whole story and one which at first quite put me off. However, I then became personally involved in the next great Three-Toes case, and I had to re-reappraise my opinion. If I have learned anything from thirty years of "monster-hunting," it is that not only is the history of events never simple and straightforward, but that a number of related, unrelated, or quite extraneous matters are invariably present, or arise in due course to cloud the issue. It is quite uncanny. Not only do the hoaxers and funsters always appear in fairly short order; there always seems to be something equally mysterious and outlandish going on locally. Get a UFO landing and invariably there'll be a fine poltergeist in operation hardby; get a good lake-monster report, and somebody finds quite another animal dead on the beach—an animal that should not be there or within thousands of miles of the place. (*Vide:* a manatee found on the shore of Lake Okanagan in Canada after several people had seen the famous Ogopogo there again.) [23] Thus it is very difficult to separate the wheat from the chaff. If somebody is found making phoney foot tracks, it does not mean that they made them all, or that the hoaxter is doing anything other than *imitating* the genuine article. What more handy for a witch-doctor than the ability to make the tracks of some terrifying beast that scared his clients but the true nature of which he knew. After reappraisal of the two versions of Mr. Lilius' story, and getting the time sequence straight, I was forced to the conclusion that there *is* some form of large, three-toed, bipedal, scaly, sea monster inhabiting that coast, and that firsthand knowledge of it had come in very handy for this nasty and dangerous old witch-doctor in promoting his murders—which he admitted were to obtain "medicine"—and to keep his flock in line. The clincher is that when caught *imitating* the tracks, the witch-doctor had left so many of his own tracks that one of Lilius' native servants had been able to track *him*, although he was not a professional hunter. The tracks found by Lilius and photographed were never accompanied by any other tracks.

So here we are back again on the same tracks and on the same continent, but confronted with a somewhat novel feature—to wit, a sort of "Chipekwe" coming out of the sea. But take heart; this is merely a novelty, not an inconsistency, and for several reasons. First, there is no doubt that many so-called dinosaurs were beach-combers of both freshwater and saltwater beaches—more especially the carnivorous ones—since a lot of their food came from sluggish swamp and aquatic animals, besides carrion washed ashore. Secondly, these types undoubtedly took first to wading, then swimming into shallow waters, even if they did *not* have webbed feet; and please note this most pertinent point as we shall come back to it very forcibly later when we meet Three-Toes, Model B. Third, and most significant of all, is the fact that throughout many enormous stretches along the east African coast the land and the sea are intimately wedded in a most extraordinary manner. Not only do innumerable rivers great and small empty into the Indian Ocean, they almost all tend to form outsized (in proportion to their volume) deltas. Then also, due to the prevailing currents being parallel to the coast, many of these river mouths turn abruptly to one side or the other upon hitting the sea. As a result of this, endless and enormous sand and gravel spits have been formed parallel to the main coast, and behind these, vast salt or brackish lagoons have formed. In time, many of these have become completely landlocked, finally turning into freshwater lagoons. Thus, basically terrestrial animals—even more so the semi-aquatic ones like crocodiles and hippos—have taken to entering and swimming considerable distances in the sea off this coast. The crocodiles there have, in fact, become almost as maritime as the true Sea Crocodile (*Crocodilus porosus*) of northern Australia at the opposite side of the Indian Ocean.

There is, therefore, no reason why a swamp animal such as the "Chipekwe," should not long ago have taken to hunting down the rivers to the seashore and have then ventured into the waves. What is more, with seventy- to eighty-million years in which to adapt, there is no reason why some of them should not have adopted the marine environment to the exclusion of the landlocked freshwater one. This does not mean that they would not hang around coasts, enter rivers and lagoons, and probably come ashore. Being reptiles, they probably reproduce through the laying of eggs which, being porous, need to be deposited in air as opposed to water, so that the developing embryos within them can obtain a continuing supply of free oxygen. Such creatures might well have come ashore to lay their eggs but, being apparently nocturnal—or coming ashore only at night—such activities on their part might well be missed. Sea-turtles come ashore at night to lay their eggs although they are otherwise completely aquatic. They dig into loose, well-aerated sand, deposit a mass of eggs therein, covering them up before going back into the sea and leaving their progeny to fend for themselves on hatching. These "chipekwe-types" might well do the same. Who has ever deliberately looked for, and especially dug for, fresh dinosaur eggs on the lonely and mostly uninhabited coasts of Tanzania, Mozambique, or even Natal? This business of coming ashore to lay eggs will crop up again, and very forcibly as we have said when we come to Three-Toes, Model B.

Ceratosaurus-type reptiles as they are presently set up as skeletons, and more so when fleshed-out as reconstructions, look more like land-living, cursorial animals of the ostrich type or at least the kangaroo type. However, a positive mass of different so-called Duck-billed dinosaurs developed at the end of the age of reptiles (the Cretaceous) and these were definitely swamp dwellers, vegetarians, and most probably swimmers.[24] Despite their silly looking legs, like those of birds and obviously made for running, they could well have had webbed feet like those of ducks and other water birds. Thus equipped, and holding their little forelegs pressed against their sides, swaying along with a side-to-side motion like the marine iguanas of the Caribbean and all other swimming reptiles, propelled by their long powerful tails, and occasionally kicking with their great webbed hind-feet, they might be just as efficient swimmers as any other aquatic animals short of whales or fish.

The area of coasts, shallows, and deeps off the eastern side of central and southeastern Africa is a very "funny" country. Off that coast are the Comoros and other odd islands with very peculiar floras and faunas. Then we have Madagascar which is a sort of living museum of animals. Finally, the limbed, coelacanth fish, *Latimeria*, turns up there. Then again, on reviewing just how much actual exploration and animal collecting has really been done in all the areas of the world, we find that this one has been sorely neglected. There are innumerable rumours of as-yet-uncaught-animals of all kinds all along this coast and notably in the forested areas to the north of Mozambique. And, if things like the okapi can remain hidden until the turn of the century in a part of Africa that has been inhabited for millenia, and whole herds of Forest Bison in Canada within a hundred miles of a new superhighway until as late as 1960, who has the audacity to say that a few modest-sized "Chipekwe," spending the day in the water with only their nostrils above water to breathe and only coming ashore at night and then possibly only during certain limited seasons to lay eggs, cannot exist in this vast unexplored area? And, what is more, dinosaurs that took to the sea might well have developed the habit of live-birth like whales.

Chapter 3.

THREE TOES—MODEL B.

AFTER THE LILIUS AFFAIR, I know of no records of old
Three-Toes turning up for ten years until the historic
outburst in Florida in February, 1948. This is a terrifically
long and involved story on which I personally prepared a
fifty-three-page report, after two weeks intensive investigation on behalf of N.B.C. and the then N.Y. *Herald
Tribune*.[25] I shall therefore confine the actual history of
events to a bare chronology in order to save mileage for a
proper analysis of the facts and a description of some
experiments that we made, the inferences gained from
these, and some legitimate speculation.

The opening gambit was the appearance overnight of a
set of tracks on the beach at a place called Clearwater
in Florida; these came out of the sea, up to a four-foot
sand bank which they apparently failed to negotiate, then
wandered about the beach a bit, and finally went back
into the water. A young couple smooching in a car on the
beach road at about 3:30 a.m. ran to the police saying
they had seen a huge monster stomp out of the sea at this
point, and begged for a rifle to shoot it. The young man
was in such an excited state that he greatly impressed the
Chief of Police. Later, when the other authorities and the
local populace saw the tracks in the morning they all
became well-nigh hysterical.

The beach was swept clean that day by the tide, but
the next night almost the same set of tracks turned up
again. Then on March 6 the first 100 yards of similar tracks
appeared a mile and a half north; then, at the north
end of Dan's Island (the next island south of Clearwater Beach) on March 20; about 350 yards of tracks at
Indian Rocks, some ten miles south of the first point, on
April 3; a mile of them on an uninhabited coast three
miles south of Indian Rocks, on April 8; and finally on
Philip's Hammock in Tampa Bay, "some time later". Old
Three-Toes then withdrew until October of that year,
when he appeared forty miles up the Suwannee River at a

place called Suwannee Gables and apparently pounded out of the river, over a low bank under the forest, into a lily-pond, then out again, down the bank, and into a slew which connected with the main river.[26]

This set of tracks was approximately 200 yards in total length and consisted of about 240 paces. For comparison with the Lilius' tracks, the imprints measured from the tip of the claw on the middle toe to the back of the heel, 13.41″ for the left foot and 13.50″ for the right foot. The distance from the tip of the outer claw to the same heel point was 10.24″ for the left, and 9.87″ for the right foot; the measurements of the inner toes was 10.91″ and 11.00″ respectively. But for the inner-toe length, the right foot on this occasion appears to be slightly larger. Such slight differences are common to almost all animals including ourselves. The stride was just 5 feet, measured from the back of the heel print on the one side to the back of the heel of the next imprint on that same side. Measuring the imprints from the heel-tip of a right foot to the heel-tip of left foot ahead of it, it was 31.00.″ I shall leave further details of both the tracks and the individual imprints for the present and complete the historical record, because this constitutes one of the most convincing cases of monster-hunting that I know of.

First, it should be noted that the Gulf coast of Florida had suffered very badly during the latter part of 1947 and early 1948 from one of the famous (or infamous) "Red Tides". These are caused by the sudden increase, or "flushing" as it is called, of certain small unicellular planktonic animals that become so numerous they discolor the whole sea, turning it red. These "flushes" are highly toxic to much other marine life and finally lethal to fish so that they die by the myriads, then float at the surface or wash ashore to bloat and rot and upset everybody. Further, the poison-chain spreads out from the "flushes" which themselves may be thousands of square miles in extent, affecting deepwater fish and larger animals which prey upon these. It was therefore very significant that Three-Toes turned up first toward the end of this natural marine disaster, just north of its periphery and *inside* the more or less landlocked Gulf.

Open-ocean dwellers wandering into the Gulf would be cut off from the Atlantic if a red tide formed a barrier inside and north of the effluent of the Gulf Stream, and this is just what had happened. Further, after milling about this periphery in March and April the three-toed track-maker(s) must have moved north, up the west Florida coast, to the mouth of the Suwannee River, and then apparently went up that river. The possible reason for their doing this will appear later.

That the animal—and I feel that on this occasion there *was* only one—was a wanderer, lost, confused, and generally "unhappy", would seem to be indicated by its actions, or alleged actions. If it had been indigenous to the area, its kind would have been well known from earliest days. It seemed to have thrown all its natural caution to the winds and it got itself seen by all manner of people on land, on the water, and under it. Its initial appearance was in Big Pass, north of Clearwater, the day before it was seen coming out of the sea and its tracks were first found at Clearwater. It was spotted in Big Pass by two professional fishermen, bobbing in and out of the surface and causing a large perturbation of the smooth sea shortly after dawn. Then, on July 25, it was spotted by two fliers, George Orfanides and John Milner from the Dunedin Flying Company airport, swimming about 200 feet off the shore of Hog Island, in crystal-clear water about eight feet deep. It was about fifteen feet long, with a "very hairy body, a heavy blunt head and back legs like an alligator but much heavier. The tail (was) long and blunt".[27]

The men returned to the airport and picked up Mario Hernandez, Director of the Flying School, and Francis Whillock, owner of the Beachcomber Restaurant at Clearwater. Flying back, they spotted the beast swimming out with the tide in about eighteen feet of water and doing an estimated eight knots. They made half a dozen passes at it and were able to see that it had four limbs but that the front ones were kept pressed under the body most of the time. The creature's next appearance was most startling. I obtained this account firsthand later in the year from a couple who had been visiting Florida in August on a fishing trip from Milwaukee.[28]

This couple had rented a small rowboat north of Tarpon Springs for a day's leisurely fishing among the innumerable small uninhabited islands and cays close inshore. They decided to land on one island and cast from shore. This island was covered with a dense growth of sea-grape bushes and some palms. Hauling their boat onto an oyster shoal, the lady waded ashore and started walking up the beach while her husband sorted out the fishing tackle. A little way along, something caught her eye in the bushes. She described it as large and gray, and, as she put it, she at first thought it might be a tent erected by some boy scouts who were on the mainland that day. However, no sooner had she passed it than her husband yelled out to her and, turning round, she got a terrible shock for a huge animal was waddling down the narrow beach into the shallow water. Both she and her husband described the animal as "having a head like a rhinoceros but with no neck. It sort of flowed into its narrow shoulders. It was gray and covered with short thick fur. It had short, very thick legs and huge feet, and from its shoulders hung two flippers. It didn't run into the water, or dive in; it sort of slid in half sidewise." (The significance of this description I am going to leave for the moment.)

Three-Toes then vanished again until shortly before its tracks were found up the Suwanee River. A Mr. Hayes, with the Deacon of the Baptist Church at nearby Cheflin, in company with others, was having a picnic lunch on the river bank when they all saw a dome-shaped, rough and knobby object which they at first thought was a log, but which was floating *upstream*. They jumped into a skiff propelled by an outboard but by the time they got this going the thing had gone round a bend up-river and they failed to come up with it.

Three days later a Mrs. Mary Belle Smith, a well-known local character who spent much of her time fishing under the bridge over the Suwannee that carries Route 19, arrived in the village of Old Town in a great state of excitement saying that, while fishing from the north bank, a very large, dun-colored animal had surfaced in front of her and had then "paddled" upstream. Next, one Martin Sharpe, a trapper who had spent his whole life on the river and at its head-waters in the Okefenokee Swamp and who, if anybody, knew all the local wildlife, reported that he had heard something "slapping" in the lily-pond where the tracks finally appeared late one night and that, on approaching with a flashlight, some animal had set up "great gurgling growls" and then had set off "running or galloping and splashing through the water", and which he insisted was "certainly larger than a horse". He was a quiet sober man and when I interviewed him he made it quite clear that he was not in the least frightened of any animal in the forest but that he was most puzzled at this. The next actual sighting of the beast was made by me about three weeks later, when flying down the river in the Herald-Tribune's plane, with pilot Lloyd Rondeau in control. I will now document the sighting in order to preserve continuity in the record.

This was one of, if not the most infuriating experiences of my life. We were flying along at about five-hundred feet trying to keep directly over the river which twists and turns like an aggravated snake. When about halfway from Suwannee Gables to the sea in an uninhabited stretch of river flanked by tall forests both of us spotted some enormous dirty-yellow colored creature roiling about on the surface of the water, making a huge lozenge-shaped patch of foam on the dark waters all around it. Of course no sooner had we spotted it than we shot around the next bend. The pilot banked madly and we whirled back, but the river was so sinuous that we overshot it and had quite a time re-finding any part of it. When we did, we weren't sure whether we were at the loop above or below the place where we had seen the animal; so we spent a long time cruising first one way and then back down the other, but we did not see the thing again. The poor pilot was absolutely enraged as he had become deeply interested in the hunt and seemed to feel that missing the river was his fault. I assured him that such was standard practice in the tropics even with the most experienced bush-pilots, but he could not be consoled. What I saw was about twelve-feet long and four-feet wide, was domed above but had some things at either end which were churning up the water. Finally, just the same thing was reported seen at a place called Dunedin on November 14, two days before I left the area.

However, the major event in this chronology was the appearance of tracks similar to those seen in southern Florida in the spring, on the banks of the Suwannee River in northern Florida, and about forty miles inland. These were first spotted early in the morning of the October 21, 1948, two days after Mr. Hayes had seen something going upstream and the night after Mrs. Mary Belle Smith had spotted the same thing somewhat farther upstream. They appeared about half a mile above the road bridge under which Mrs. Smith had been fishing, on the left or west bank of the river, going upstream. The physical features of the locale must be given in considerable detail, otherwise the significance of the finding will mean very little.

The tracks were found at a point about halfway between two bridges over the Suwannee River—the northern one carrying the railroad track between Cross City and Gainesville, the southern one carrying Route 19 from Old Town to Cheflin. The stretch of river here develops a large semicircular bend to the westward and is flanked by virgin swamp forest which extends back from the river about half a mile on the west bank and for some four miles on the east side. This swamp forest is backed by a belt of dry, pine stands with numerous contained swamps. Beyond this, agricultural and cleared land commences and extends for a considerable distance in both directions. The Suwannee River above this point is flanked with swamp and other types of forest throughout its two-hundred-fifty mile course right to its source in the Okefenokee Swamp of Georgia. Going downstream from Suwannee Gables it is likewise flanked on either side by an increasingly wide belt of coastal swamp forest.

The soil throughout the area is sandy, often, in fact, pure sand, even in the forest. At the point where the tracks occurred there is a scattering of dark loam and leaf-mould among the roots of trees on the river bank, but a few paces inland the surface is composed of pure sand. This "ball-bearing sand", as it is called, is extremely fine and white and easily disturbed when dry, but it flattens out and becomes almost as hard and solid as concrete when wet. Even a light rain renders it so hard that a heavy truck can pass over it without leaving any tread marks at all, and such were the conditions when the tracks occurred after two weeks of rain and considerable flooding from the river. This is of special significance. Beyond this strip of sand, which forms a natural levee along the river side, the ground drops several feet by a gentle slope, and is covered with about two to three inches of springy, fibrous loam with patches of bare mud.

The whole area is covered by a fairly tall closed-canopy of large trees and the undergrowth is very sparse, consisting of only a few lean briars, thin-stemmed bushes, a few saplings, and some short grass which grows in damp depressions. The land descends gradually for some two hundred feet to a large, lily-filled swamp in which large cypresses grow, and which is fed by a number of enormous clear-water springs that boil up in deep holes. At the point where the tracks occurred, an intermediate shallow wedge of dirty swamp known locally as a "slew", filled with trees and small-stemmed tall bushes, extends northward between the river and the lily-swamp. This connects with the latter two miles downstream and the combined outflow enters the main river half a mile beyond.

The area covered by the tracks was contained within a rectangle roughly three-hundred-fifty feet along the river bank, and two-hundred-twenty feet between the river and the lily-swamp. The actual tracks appeared to come out of the river up a little cleft in the bank, then they crossed to the lily-swamp by a fairly direct route, taking approximately 104 paces of an average of 31.00″ each. They then emerged again from the same point and recrossed the forest and the sand road by a direct line, apart from some deviations to avoid vegetation, and entered the dirty swamp or slew. The track-maker appeared to have passed southward down the slew for some sixty paces and then emerged on the right side, climbed a gentle incline, circumnavigated some tangled bushes, overcame a small fallen tree-trunk which was extensively scarred as if some large heavy body had been dragged over it. The tracks became lost in a grass-filled depression but then appeared again and went directly to the lily-swamp once more, where they led to a large, fallen, hollow and rotten tree. This was crushed absolutely flat in the middle, leaving a passage four feet wide under an arch five feet high through the bushes, and leading directly out into the lily pond beyond, where a large circular area was churned up, all the lily pads being uprooted. In all, the track-maker must have taken approximately 242 paces and covered about 200 yards on land. It must have left the pond by the stream joining the slew and entering the main river.

In order to obtain exact data on the form and stride of the tracks, the longest series of still visible imprints that remained on the muddy floor of the forest was selected and mapped on a one-inch scale by normal surveying methods. A more or less continuous series of seventeen imprints was found, of which only three were blurred and one completely absent, coinciding, as it must have done, with a tree root.

Without detailed examination of any individual imprints, it is impossible to state categorically that the tracks are those of a two-legged or a four-legged creature. From first appearances it seemed that the maker was on this occasion two-legged. Assuming this to be so for the moment, we may ascertain the average stride. This may be expressed in one of three ways—i.e., either as the distance between two imprints of the same foot; directly between the heels of consecutive left or right feet; or, as the distance between the heel imprints of two consecutive feet along the base line of direction of the trackmaker's progress. By the first expression, the stride is on an average just 5 feet; by the second, 31″ from heel tip to heel tip, and by the third, 25″. The width of the track was on an average only 15″; that is to say, the left-hand imprints lay in a line 15″ to the left of the right-hand imprints when they ran in a straight line. This accords more nearly with the tracks of a large mammal than with those of any known dinosaur of comparable size, but it is much more *birdlike.*

However, there was considerable variation in the length of stride, and mostly in accordance with differences in the gradient of the surface. First, imprints Nos. 1 to 4, and 13 to 17 in the series studied, are somewhat longer spaced. These were on distinct downgrades. The stride between Nos. 4 and 8, however, is strangely compressed. These were in a little depression at the end of a small fallen log. Further, at another point the tracks negotiated a five-foot rise up a gentle slope by following an S-shaped course, and here the stride was reduced to about twelve inches in the forward line, but spread to two feet in width. This is certainly in accord with the actions of a heavy animal on such a gradient. It was further to be noted—and this could only be seen well in half light—that whenever the imprints started downhill after a rise or a level, there was a considerable scattering of white, river or swamp mud (quite unlike the surrounding black loam) sprinkled around the imprints. (This mud figures again below, in the special imprint entitled imprint "x".)

Finally, from the scaled plan of all the imprints forming the track, certain facts as to angle of incidence of feet to direction of travel may be inferred, but it will be seen from this that the feet invariably turn slightly outward from the direction of travel. Fewer right-hand imprints than left-hand ones were perfect enough for analysis, yet the variation in the right in this respect was much more noticeable. Moreover, two of the right imprints—Nos. 6 and 14—appear to be at a strangely incongruous angle. In the former case (No. 6) the foot is grossly turned to the right and outwards; in the latter (No. 14), it is turned to the left or inwards, despite the fact that the track-maker was commencing to turn to the left in the former case and to the right in the latter. No such discrepancies occur with the left foot, which throughout seems to be much more sure-footed.

Taken as a whole, the most significant features of the tracks were such as might be both noticeable and notable only to an experienced woodsman, hunter, or animal-tracker. These were the manner in which the tracks invariably followed the gentlest gradients even at the cost of considerable meandering and, secondly, that they meticulously avoided all possible snags or obstacles even down to the smallest bushes. Further, the imprints were carefully placed on the most resilient ground and avoided bare roots. These are, one and all, typically animal traits, especially those of night-roaming animals which, like tigers for instance, always prefer a path to walk upon and avoid brushing against bushes or even herbs if possible.

Tests were made on the course of the tracks by blindfolding an experimenter who then followed the easiest way by testing the gradient with his feet, and by avoiding other obstacles by sense of touch with legs and arms. The course thus traversed proved to coincide exactly with that of the tracks, though there were several much easier paths open to him and easily passable. In fact, the actual path of the tracks often went under low branches that necessitated the man's bending almost double. Such was the case at the point where the small log was scarified.

It was, however, when we came to an intimate study of the individual imprints themselves that we found ourselves confronted with some facts that could only be rationalized on the theory that they had been made by an animal. In taking measurements of these imprints one difficulty was encountered; namely, to ascertain exactly what point on the "bow" of the heel-impression-edge to take as a starting point. This bow was almost a semicircle and in many cases the point chosen could vary one way or the other by as much as three-quarters of an inch. This was ascertained by having a number of people make a series of choices; and most of the toe measurements were taken from a compromise of these choices.

Eight left and five right imprints were selected and, within the limits of careful measurement in quarter-inches, made possible by the exceedingly sharp forward notches of the "claws", they averaged

Left Imprints		*Right Imprints*	
Outer	10.24	Outer	9.87
Middle	13.41	Middle	13.50
Inner	10.91	Inner	11.00

From this it appeared that the outer toe of the left foot was over a third-of-an-inch longer than the right outer toe. The middle toes were probably almost identical, as were the inner. The imprints measured were selected as carefully as possible to exclude those displaying excessive "slip".

The imprints were impressed into the ground to varying depths according to the nature of the soil. Some found under water in muddy sand were said to have been two inches deep; one in soft sand which was inspected by us was at least two inches deep all over; those in firm mud were about an inch and a half deep in the middle of the ball of the foot; on loamy soil they appeared to have been pressed in to a depth of about three quarters of an inch; but there were imprints that only just dented the ground and still others in which only the toe tips and claws were deeply gouged into the earth. These last were most noticeable on the bank where no heel impressions were left at all but where the claws had gouged slots three inches deep on the side of the bank. We were told by several people who had observed the tracks when fresh—and these included the local police—that the imprints were originally clearly defined on the hardest sand, although we were unable to make any impression on this by stamping or even by throwing a 35-pound lead model of the imprints down upon it from a height of three feet.

All of these facts at first appeared to be consistent with the theory that the imprints had been *stamped* rather than impressed into the ground but we were later to learn, as a result of a series of experiments carried out on the spot, that this could *not* have been the case. At the same time, another curious fact came to light. Although there was slight evidence of forward thrust, there was no noticeable example of *slip* except in the case of what we called Imprint "x", which was a special case. However, there was ample evidence of slight twist in many of the prints. Strangely, the claws do not seem to have shifted but rather the heel of the feet, which always slewed inwards. Captain Carlos Musgrove of the Highway Patrol, who conducted a very thorough inspection on his own of the fresh tracks, showed us his measurements, and these clearly indicated that the left foot exerted more forward thrust than the right.

The general impression of the imprints is one of remarkable "pudginess", and many people have observed on seeing them for the first time that they look quite unnatural because they lack any indication of toe-jointing, pads, or "heel". On closer inspection, and as will be explained in a moment, this is not truly the case. They indeed at first looked somewhat formless and, in fact, resembled in general outline the impressions left by an Emperor Penguin more than anything else.

Perhaps the most significant feature of all in these mysterious imprints is the variation in the form of the toes and their remarkable and apparently quite illogical disposition. As will be seen from the measurements given above, the feet are almost exact "mirrors", though the left outer toe might be somewhat longer than the right. The toes are not, however, similar. The measurements *excluding* the claws are as follows: Outer, 9¼"; Middle, 12"; Inner, 8½", for the left foot; the reverse for the right foot. The shortest toe is therefore the inner on both feet but it has the longest claw, one of 2½"; the middle toe is the longest and bears a claw intermediate in length, of 1½"; the outer toe is intermediate in length but bears the shortest claw, only 1" long. This is an exact reversal of the arrangement found in the fossil tracks of *Theropod* dinosaurs, but it is exactly in accord with the arrangement as seen in such birds as the Ratite Cassowaries, and more so the penguins.

There are, however, other complications. First, the form of the claws would appear to be very different on the three toes. That on the inner toe was narrow, long, and sharp; that on the middle toe was intermediate in length but always sharply incised into the earth, while that on the outer toe was wide, short, and blunt. Consideration of the longitudinal section of the toe imprints would seem to indicate that the deep transverse grooves immediately behind the so-called "claw" impressions actually represented the bases of the claws rather than the tips of the toes.

Plaster casts made from the fresh tracks showed distinctly the middle toe bulged over to the left-hand side, and one left-hand foot impression did so to the extent that the claw imprint was no less than 20° from the perpendicular, while the other two toes had apparently remained upright, the inner toe even seeming to incline slightly inward. (How this could have been accomplished by a rigid device made of metal or other solid substance, if these tracks were manmade, is more than simple reason can conceive.) Similar sidewise "bulging" either to one side or the other, occurred in imprints Nos. 4, 9, and 11, contained in the measured set of seventeen imprints.

Another inexplicable fact is the positive evidence of variability in the angle of incidence between the toes. A series of measurements was made to show the variation of distance between the toe tips. These measurements are very precise because of the extremely sharp angle formed by the claw tips in the plastic soil. Measurement of the full series of the seventeen selected tracks showed the following variations in the spread of the tips of the three toes: Left outer to middle toe: 1"; left inner to middle toe: 1½"; right inner to middle toe: none; right middle to outer toe: ½". Again the left foot appears to have carried the major part of the work and to have reacted more strongly in various ways. From this it may be inferred that the toes spread outward to a varying degree. Again one would like to know what manner of manmade device could produce such effects and still be rigid enough to make these impressions.

A third and even more surprising discovery was that the middle toe could on occasion be held up by a root while the outer and inner toes not only reached the ground but gouged deep claw incisions into its surface. This is manifestly impossible of reproduction with any rigid device. More curious still was imprint "x", which appeared as an isolated imprint on the track leading back from the lily-swamp to the slew. This showed distinct evidence of slip. A stick on an average of ¾" in diameter had been lying on the forest floor for some time before the tracking took place, as shown by a series of ant tunnels excavated in the mud below it throughout its length which were heavily coated with green algae and moss. This stick had been snapped off and the bark freshly scoured. A coating of whitish-grey mud, not from the forest floor but matching the lily-swamp bottom when dried, was plastered over the stick, and the inner toe of the imprint had spread out and been imprinted *under* the stick. Finally, 2½″ inch piles of forest-floor loam had been forced up alongside. These were not found accompanying any other tracks and would appear to have been produced by forward thrust. How these could have occurred without some form of *webs* between the toes is hard to understand.

Finally, we were told by all those who inspected the tracks when fresh (including the local police and state troopers) that all the imprints in sand, both soft and hard, showed small spurts of sand thrown back by the claws into the middle of the imprints. This we could not verify at the late date when our inspection was made, but some corollary observations bore out the same general principle. Where the tracks emerged from the slew, the stride constricted greatly, as has been explained, and the individual imprints showed no ball or heel impressions at all. At the same time, the three claws were very deeply incised into the earth—here composed of short grassroots and loam—to a depth of 3½″ in one case of a middle toe. This concludes the positive evidence derived from scientific examination of the tracks and individual imprints.

We then turned to experimentation with a view to finding out if possible how these could have been made by man or a machine. This was hard for some of us because we were by this time almost convinced that we had sufficient proof of their being made by an animal but fortunately we had with us serious-minded, highly intelligent and knowledgeable people who remained skeptical of this notion. What is more, they whipped up considerable enthusiasm among all of us so that the experiments became a sort of competition—a very healthy plan when indulging scientific enquiry. The skeptics thought up a whole string of possibilities, and we then took each in turn and tried them out in their presence and that of a third group who were entirely neutral in the matter. The results were very startling.

The obvious and logical explanation of the origin of any tracks such as are herein described is that they were manmade, either as a pure hoax or for some definite publicity purposes. The very idea that an unknown animal large enough to have made such imprints could be wandering around even in such a comparatively unopened part of Florida would appear to be complete nonsense. Moreover, everybody—except those very few who had taken the trouble to examine the tracks in detail—naturally subscribed to this opinion and therefore either did not know, or tended to ignore, details like those that have been described above and which at least seemed to cast some serious doubt upon the possibility that they could have been made either by a man or a machine. In favor of such an opinion there are, however, a number of consequential facts.

The tracks first appeared on a number of well-frequented resort beaches. Then they appeared on a road at the end of an unique tourist attraction called the "Jungle Drive". But, against this must be placed the fact that no less than four of the original southern Florida cases, and the tracks at Dunedin in northern Florida, were found on completely uninhabited beaches that are seldom visited even by fishermen. Secondly, it is only at resorts on the ocean coast, and only at this one spot on the lower reaches of the Suwannee River that *any* people inspect the terrain regularly. Thousands of tracks could have appeared and then disappeared through natural agencies along the coast and all up and down the Suwannee River banks without anybody ever having come across any of them. Further, unless one were specifically looking for them, or knew of their previous occurrence, nobody—not even an experienced trapper—would even notice these tracks unless they lay prominently out on some open area, because they were so completely unlike anything that is commonly encountered.

Points in favor of the theory that the tracks are manmade must of necessity constitute reasons why they could not have been made by an animal. Presumably, almost anything that can be done by an animal could be reproduced by men, given time and patience. If the tracks, therefore, displayed features that could not have been made by an animal, it could be safely felt that one could assume they were made by men. Subsequent developments showed that we had been altogether too hasty in our assumptions, because the very things that we singled out as appearing to have been impossible for an animal to create proved to be even more impossible for a man to have executed.

First, we had thought that all the tracks were too perfect, but we then found that they were not so. They varied by thrust and slip, by the angle of incidence to the main direction of tracking, by the angle of incidence of the toes, in their stride—and in exact accord with a natural animal stride—and in the proportional stride between left and right tracks on turns—again as in normal animal tracks. There were said to have been sand "kicks" in the fresh tracks; the toes bulged or turned over individually, and in either direction. Further, it was first assumed that the stride was ridiculously short for an animal of the size indicated by the depth of the imprints, but it was then pointed out that a Penguin, for instance, takes very short strides.

The complete absence of any tail-drag or of any indication of forefeet prompted us to speculate as to how any animal could maintain balance on up-and-down slopes as well as on the level ground, but there are many living animals beside man that can do so. Any argument against an animal having made these tracks, based upon this consideration, also holds true for man—especially when he is equipped with heavy foot impedimenta. There is, in fact, nothing that we have been able to single out that might conclusively prove or even strongly indicate that the tracks were made by a man rather than by an animal.

The animal would obviously have to be a wanderer in Florida, out of its natural element and perhaps lost. Its ridiculous-looking, three-toed, apparently jointless foot would not be at all useless to an aquatic animal *if it had a web between the toes*. The imprint is, in fact, very much like that of a vast penguin, whose toes are webbed. A duck's tracks often do not show any trace of the webbing on soft mud, whereas there is distinct evidence of webbing in at least one imprint examined—namely, imprint "x". Those who believe that the tracks were made by an animal (and it must be stressed that, though these are few in number, they are the very persons who have examined the tracks in detail, in some cases for months and almost invariably with a very critical eye) point out a number of very difficult questions. These are as follows: (1) The enormous extent of the tracks: 220 yards on the Suwannee River banks; 300 yards; a-mile-and-a-half; 600 yards; and so on about Clearwater, and all appearing overnight. (2) The complete absence of any other tracks accompanying them, either human or of machines. (3) The depth that they are impressed into sand that a heavy man could not indent more than a fraction of an inch, and which, when wet, receives no impression made by man or by a heavy truck (i.e., a moving wheel). (4) The apparently haphazard, though animal-like, meanderings of the tracks, approaching low banks and apparently trying unsuccessfully to negotiate them, the wandering back and forth along a beach. (5) That they always appear to come out of the sea or a river and go back into the sea or a swamp. (6) That they have appeared on frequented beaches as well as at places that are seldom visited and sometimes not normally inspected for years on end. (7) That many people have reported unknown animals of large size in the areas where the tracks appear and nowhere else. (8) The impossibility, as they see it, of men making the tracks for various of the above reasons.

To these points we must add some of our own observations. First and foremost is the almost uncanny accuracy in every detail of the hoax, if it is a hoax. That any man or body of men could know so much about wild animal life as to make the tracks in just the manner that they appear, but that they also should be able to carry this out time and time again at night without anybody seeing them or giving them away, (in the Suwanee River case) under the closed canopy of the forest trees, although it was a full moon (and we inspected the locale under the next full moon to ascertain this fact) is frankly incredible. Not only are the tracks perfect in themselves, but they follow an extraordinary pattern: the stride contracting or elongating at bends just as it should do if produced by a large, heavy animal, the toes only appearing on banks, the heel more profoundly on downgrades; the angle of incidence of the imprints changing on turns in one way when the right foot was used as a pivot, in another when the left happened to be foremost; the toes spreading or bulging over individually just when they should do so time after time.

Secondly, the choice of route is extraordinary for any man to take. Why should a man avoid tiny bushes when he could quite well step over or on them, and meticulously follow the easiest gradients *invariably*, when we know from the evidence of the imprints themselves and from the tracks as a whole that he could easily have surmounted much steeper slopes. The route followed was invariably just that which an animal would follow and says almost too much for the acumen of the hoaxer.

Thirdly, the matter of weight presents the greatest problem. If made by a man, either a machine must have been used or the person must have carried the weight himself and performed the act physically. A machine could not have been used because it would have left some tracks other than those imprints seen in the soft mud at the margin of the lily-swamp and the slew, unless it were a large and elaborate mechanical device. If this had been taller than five-feet, or wider than two-feet-six-inches, however, it could not have passed between the fragile bushes and plants that bordered the route that the tracks followed. Further, no machine is known that can either alter the diameter of a wheel while in motion, or contract a tread so that length of stride can be made to vary in two manners at once, in the same manner at once, or in one manner at a time, as occurred with the right and left strides. The alternative is a helicopter, which is ridiculous because it would have been spotted on the beach immediately opposite the town of Clearwater, even at night, and it could not in any case have penetrated the closed canopy of the forest on the Suwannee River.

If made physically by a man, either with devices strapped to his feet or on stilts, how did he carry a ton on each leg—the absolute minimum that the road engineers said could have made the imprints even in soft ground? He manifestly could not, and besides, a man on stilts could not have passed under the trees and bushes on the Suwannee banks. The only remaining suggestion is that the imprints must have been stamped rather than pressed in. And this is what we had assumed to have occurred when we first gave it as our opinion that the tracks *could* be manmade. However, actual experiment showed this to be impossible and for one very simple reason.

When we attempted to reproduce them with 35-pound lead models strapped to the writer's feet, no impression whatsoever was left on the ball-bearing sand when it was wet, and impressions made in medium or soft mud were surrounded by an impact ridge that completely surrounded the imprint. No such ridge at any time appeared around any imprint at Clearwater, on the Suwannee, or elsewhere. Instead, *pressure cracks* radiated, from the inside out, all around the periphery.

In whatever manner these imprints were made, therefore, they must have been accomplished by the downward exertion of enormous pressure, evenly and slowly applied, and not by *stamping*. How any device of sufficient weight to impress such tracks to the depth observed in the variety of soils inspected, how it was introduced to the location, unobserved, and moved along the tracks that were there for all to see, is quite beyond the comprehension of this writer, of the local police, and of all others who investigated the matter.

Finally, we cannot conceive of material rigid enough to impress the imprints, especially the tapering toes and claws, that could at the same time be pliable enough to allow one toe to rest off the ground on a root while the other two, on either side, impacted upon the ground and left imprints, and yet could spread by as much as 15° and slip under small sticks. We also learned by actual experiment that it is impossible to climb the banks and follow the original tracks with lead devices strapped to one's feet—and to leave deep toe-incisions only. When we experimented we obtained *no* toe impressions at all. The whole weight descended upon the heel, leaving a deep round indent and throwing up a large impact ridge *behind*. There was no such heel mark or impact ridge on any of the banks.

We asked our engineer friends to design a machine that could do such a job. They actually tried working for two days and nights, arguing so hotly that they kept us awake in a cabin at the other end of the line! They finally came up with a sort of Rube Goldberg device (on paper) but made it quite clear when they showed it to us that it would not work—and for two very good reasons. First, they could not invent anything that would perform all the movements that the toes had been proved to have made; and, second, the thing would have to be about fifty feet tall! They didn't even go into the likely cost. In fact, the whole idea of the phenomenon having been created by a machine was *reductio ad absurdum*. Therefore, short of the Almighty Himself or some force of a ghostly nature, the only alternate left was an animal. But what kind of animal? And this brings us to the zoological problem.

At first sight the tracks looked like those of certain dinosaurs which left their imprints in various soft surfaces subsequently buried and fossilized. However, as mentioned before, the arrangement of the toes and the claws on the toes did not jibe with any known type of dinosaur track. Then, no three-toed dinosaur is known to have been marine in habitat, though some that were semi-aquatic possibly entered brackish water and lived along coasts. Some of these may have had webbed feet, it is true. Another factor militating against this suggestion is, of course, the fact that no living dinosaur is known and not one single bone of one has been found in any rock since the end of the Cretaceous Period, some seventy-million years ago. On the other hand, nobody had found a single bone of a Coelacanth in those rocks and yet they turned up one alive in 1938—and right off Mr. Lilius' coast, to boot.

The fact that no *Theropod* dinosaur has turned up alive does not necessarily mean that there are none still in existence. And there really are an astonishing number of reports, and often from seemingly unimpeachable witnesses, that some still *do* exist, notably (as already explained) in several parts of central and east Africa, also in Malaya, and in New Guinea. Mr. Lilius' creature certainly sounds like a reptile, allegedly having scales, a long tapering tail, small front paws, and a head "like a huge turtle." Some dinosaur skulls, seen from the side, look astonishingly like vast turtles. If there are relic dinosaurs about twenty feet long with bodies no bigger than donkeys still living in the swamps of Mozambique, one of them might well wander down to the coast from time to time, then splash about in a brackish lagoon behind the sand dunes. That is as far as we can go with the dinosaurian spectre.

With the Florida case we have much more solid grounds for speculation. And here, all the different descriptions tally, but for one small point—and all these lead in one direction—that is, to the one class of animals that have the kind of feet to make the tracks and prints observed. You may have noticed that, time and time again, points of likenesses to *birds* have cropped up. This may sound to you as balmy as it at first did to me. Who ever heard of a fifteen-foot bird? But, come to think of it, almost everybody has—for example, the largest species of Moa from New Zealand! This, moreover, had three toes that were used for standing, though there was a little one behind that did not reach the ground. However, all the moas were land animals as far as we know, having long thin necks and long legs like an ostrich with very small heads. The arrangement of their toes and of the claws on their toes was nothing like the Florida imprints. The moas' distant relatives, the Cassowaries, however, do have just this arrangement, and so do another group of primitive birds—the Penguins.

These, moroever, are almost wholly aquatic. They also have curiously large (for their size) and pudgy feet, short legs, so taking short strides, and they have a pair of "sort of flippers hanging from their shoulders". What is more, the heads of some species with short deep bills, when seen from the side, do look astonishingly like miniature rhinoceroses' heads. Nor is that all. Penguins have various methods of swimming; in some cases, they place their two feet together and hold them rigidly out behind as rudders. Seen from above, the feet look like a fairly long but stubby tail, just as the fliers described the tail of the Florida Three-Toes as seen from the air.

What better description of a giant penguin than that given by the lady from Milwaukee? "It waddled down the beach"; "It had no neck, the head just sort of flowed into the shoulders"; "It had kind of flippers hanging from its shoulders"; "It sort of slid into the water sidewise"; "It had short legs and very big feet". It also lacked a true tail. Looked at the other way, what other kind of animal (or even of bird) could it be? Furthermore, "It walked leaning forward like a duck". Many people have gagged over its alleged "hairiness". Birds don't have hairs, they have feathers. Nonetheless, the majority of non-naturalists on first seeing a penguin invariably assume that it is clothed in fur. The short, closely packed, primitive feathers look astonishingly like fur when the bird is standing, but in the water the feathers fluff out and look very hairy. Penguins come out onto land and onto ice and they can make long treks inland, but they have great difficulty in negotiating even quite low banks. To get under things they can tip down almost to the ground without toppling forward, so that a fifteen-foot job could easily have crept through the five-foot tall archway in the brush leading to the lily-pond up the Suwannee.

This was our deduction from a very long analysis of all the evidence we could accumulate and it was most strangely supported by two subsequent events.

I took the plaster casts, moulages, my lead copies of the tracks, photographs, and all the charts, maps, and plans back with me to New York. I also dug up the best of the prints, complete, cutting all around so as to leave it on a truncated pyramid of earth and then sliding a large piece of plywood under it and building a box around this. I arrived with my precious load in the Palaeontological Department of the American Museum of Natural History, to present these specimens to Dr. Edwin H. Colbert, head of that department, but I happened to hit the moment when a group of scientists from New Zealand walked in. They took one look at the original track and, with one accord, said "My God, bigger than ours". At first I naturally thought they meant bigger than their little Macquerie Penguins but then they explained that: No, they meant a Giant Penguin that they had just finished extracting (in the form of a fossil skeleton) from the rocks forming the roof of a cave, before they left New Zealand, which was *seven feet tall*.[29] We have today the three-foot tall Emperor and King Penguins; now we know there were seven-foot ones alive once in New Zealand; why not one just twice that size? Why indeed, for there is no limit to size in the water, and bulkier things than a 15-foot penguin come out on land—such as the walrus and the sea-elephant.

But the last nail to be driven into this coffin came later when a friend drew my attention to an early description of the Kerguelen Islands in the Antarctic south of the Indian Ocean.[30] The lower slopes of this island are in places covered with tall, enormous, thick, tangled bushes. (The islands are almost perpetually shrouded in mists and certain hardy vegetation grows luxuriantly in this.) They are inhabited by myriads of sea birds, many of which rest and nest in under this dense scrub. However, leading to the enclosed nesting places, which stank to high heaven of dead birds, excrement, and rotten eggs, were endless tunnels. Most of these were local-bird-sized, but some were *four-feet wide and six-feet tall!* What bird, or other animal, needs a passageway that size and shape? We just don't know of any.

Finally, be it noted that most of the reports of Three-Toes hail from the southern hemisphere and penguins are southern-hemisphere animals, though one species lives on the Galapagos Islands just north of the Equator. Further, all penguins spend most of their lives on the high seas, congregating once a year at special places and often on distant islands to breed. They are shy creatures when at sea and they float just below the surface with their heads sticking out, and usually duck under and swim long distances when they feel the throb of an approaching propellor. There could be thousands of giant penguins afloat in the Antarctic and sub-Antarctic oceans and a modern powered ship would never get near enough to them to spot them. And it is interesting to note that not a few descriptions of the heads of alleged "great sea-serpents" were, in the olden days of sail, described as looking like those of horses, camels, or rhinoceroses. A thick-billed penguin, fifteen feet long, on the coast of Florida is admittedly pretty horrid, but I don't think we can legitimately any longer laugh it out of court.

Chapter 4.

MAVERICK MOAS

IN 1960 A MINOR HUBBUB that only just avoided becoming an uproar arose in New Zealand. The avoidance was occasioned by deliberate suppression which for once was heartily endorsed by forteans and should be applauded by all. The incident that occasioned the narrow squeak in 1960 was duplicated in 1968 but this time with some at least alleged—and please watch out for these qualifying words—corollary evidence which itself replicated quite a history of discoveries of a more concrete nature. Subject at issue: Moas.[31]

Before going into the business in detail, I would like to explain the above paragraph a bit more explicitly. When an allegation of something of outstanding interest and novelty crops up, especially in the fields of the natural sciences, people tend to go a bit balmy, and this can do inestimable harm to future investigation and search. Take the case of the beloved Loch Ness Monsters. Several people in all innocence and sincerity stated that about 1933 when the first road around the loch was opened, they had seen some things, with long necks and small heads and exhibiting humps on their backs, sort of frolicking around in the waters. The immediate result was a tremendous uproar which did not subside until today and which has caused more bitterness and outright chicanery than almost anything else in the zoological field during the past century. People, ranging all the way from scientists to dopes, immediately divided into two violently opposed camps—one *pro* and the other *con* acceptance of the fact, or even the possibility, of there being a tribe of very large as-yet-unidentified animals living in said loch. The simple truth of the matter is that the rumpus was initiated, and quite unwittingly, by the initiators going-off "half-cocked". What was worse, they were what are so scathingly called "amateurs" or "non-specialists" by the professionals and self-appointed experts.

In the case of which we now speak, the initial reports were very fortunately made by some real professionals and true experts of the very departments of investigation most concerned. Knowing only too well the very real danger, both to themselves personally and to the acquisition of knowledge generally, these people refused to allow their statements to be published or their names to be attached to their stories. While this was, and is, a most judicious attitude to adopt, it unfortunately casts a considerable aura of mystery around the whole business, and this tends to make the public suspicious and the scientific community terribly cagey. Since the reporters are all of that community, a thundering silence is perhaps the best procedure for now. In this case, however, it is even more desirable as, for once, it is *not* being accompanied by masterful inactivity. Moreover, more than just something has actually been done about the matter already, and more has been initiated. What we need is absolute proof; in this case, this is actually possible for once.

Just like the Loch Ness Monsters, this business has been going on for centuries—though not specifically for *quite* as many years, since Europeans only got to the locale some two hundred years ago. Perhaps this is somewhat of a

prevarication because, when we did arrive, we were sub-
jected to quite a bombardment of tradition from the
aboriginal Maoris, just as the stupid Lowlanders, English,
and other Sassenachs were bombarded by the Heeland
Scots, who are after all the proper "natives" of their
country. Unlike Loch Ness the matter of Moas was assumed to have been permanently laid to rest, as it were,
long before said arrival of said palefaces in New Zealand.
That there had once been flightless birds, some of enormous size, on the islands and contemporary with the
ancestors of the Maoris was ingrained in local folklore but,
as usual, the stupid whites took these traditions for *myths*
which are something quite different. It was not until
comparatively recent times that the reality of this early
association was admitted, and it is only very recently that
it has been realized that this association may have continued well into colonial times; that story is in itself a most
fascinating and not altogether unfortean one, but it is
nothing compared to the fascination of one particular
aspect of it. This falls into the category of the *unexplained*
merely because it has not as yet been concluded; but for
once there is a perfectly simple and logical explanation at
hand.

Late in 1967 a government naturalist visited the forested
fjordlands of the South Island of New Zealand in an
official capacity. His duties included actual exploration of
these vast unmapped mountains and the surveying of an
enormous wildlife reserve. The reserve was created in
1950 to protect a five-hundred-acre central area in which
the Takahe (*Notornis hochstetteri*)—a large, vividly
coloured, flightless rail—had been rediscovered when it
was thought to have been extinct for over half a century.[82] This area is uninhabited and not crossed or even
penetrated by hunters or others. It was the last retreat of
a certain small subtribal group of the *Early Maoris* who
were driven from fertile lowlands to the north by a combi-
nation of the *Later Maoris* and the early white colonists.
These poor people seem to have died out during the last
century, but evidence of their occupation has been found
there, as we shall see in a moment. Simply stated, this
man reported that he had seen definite, concrete, fresh
evidence of the continued existence of a small species of
Moa during his trip.

His statement seconded a report of an alleged visual

sighting of a *live* moa in the same area by another trained zoologist in 1960 (the initial story that I mentioned at the opening of this discussion as having caused a minor hub-bub). Both parties—and they are not the same—particularly desire that their reports not be issued since they have no photographs to substantiate them, no plaster casts of spoor they say they found, and no satisfactory radiocarbon dating of some bones and feathers. The last were found in circumstances that could well be misleading; while they looked absolutely fresh, they could have lain around in the curiously dry dust of a cave (in an excessively wet area of really enormous annual rainfall—up to two-hundred inches) for a very long time; and, there was the overwhelming likelihood of "contamination". And this introduces the second set of "evidence" regarding the possible continued existence of at least one small form of moa. This story must now be told.

There was a time when nobody believed that any humans had been contemporary with living moas, but a chance discovery in 1939 by a young student of a certain Dillon's Point Primary School, named Jim Eyles, destroyed this misconception for good. Later, it became manifest that some species of moas had existed until shortly before the first white men arrived, and that they may have continued to exist until as late as the nineteenth century. The next phase was initiated by this rediscovery of the Takahe or *Notornis*, at which time even the most skeptical were considerably shaken—principally because skeptics, and notably zoological ones, simply cannot conceive of the amount of true wilderness that still exists everywhere. Then a discovery was made right in this Takahe area that brought everybody up sharp.

This was reported in a splendid little booklet entitled "Moas and Moa-Hunters" by Dr. Roger Duff, Director of the Canterbury Museum, and published by the Government Printer, in Wellington, N.Z. in 1957.[33] Speaking of a tribal-group of Maoris known as the "Ngati-mamoe" who were driven into these mountains about 1700, Dr. Duff states: "But not only the *Notornis* still lived in those mountains. In hidden valleys the fugitives encountered small groups of a small forest-dwelling moa (*Megalapteryx*) which had survived, like *Notornis*, long after the extermination of its fellows elsewhere. It is likely that the Ngati-mamoe rapidly destroyed the small colonies of

Megalapteryx, but a doubt remains—some may have out-
lived the Ngati-mamoe, *some may still survive* [Italics
mine]." It is now stated that a previous discovery by a Mr.
Ken Miers in 1949, the one of 1959, *and* this new one of
1968 were all of remains of this same *Megalapteryx*. The
1949 discovery included some bones of a bird that had
obviously been butchered and eaten; some of these were
engraved with a series of very fine deep cuts that could
probably have been made only by a metal knife. But Dr.
Duff goes on to say of this: "Even if the cuts were from a
stone flake, the date could not be earlier than the early
seventeen hundreds [why, is not explained] when the
Ngati-mamoe fled there. By either reckoning, Megalapteryx
was alive so recently that *we must seriously regard the
possibility of his [its] existence today* [Italics mine]."

The largest known extinct Moa (*Dinornis maximus*)
stood over six feet at the shoulder and, if it carried its long
neck aloft like the ostriches and its other living relatives, it
would have been well over twelve feet tall. (One would
naturally like to corral such a creature.) It was a lowland,
grass-grazing animal and could not survive in rugged,
forested mountains. Its little relative, this *Megalapteryx* if
found, would, as the excellent Dr. Duff points out, be
rather a disappointment to the average person. It would
be only about three feet tall and shaped rather like the
littler Kiwi, but with a longer neck, a great broad bill,
considerable bulk, and probably (as Dr. Bernard Heuvelmans has reconstructed it) have a sort of "baggy pants" of
primitive feathers reaching almost to the ground. Nonetheless, it would be nice to get a genuine moa, however
small and ungainly, just to confuse the skeptics, if nothing
else. And there is really no reason why we shouldn't, as
those mountains really are wild in all senses of that word.

But this is not the whole story since there is a lot of
confirmatory evidence that some moas coexisted with people in this region. When the first search for the *Notornis*
was on, an overhanging rock-cliff was found, and in a
great mound of rubbish, dust, and loam under it were
discovered: "Hundreds of feathers of the extinct moa,
kakapo, kiwi, weka, and takahe" (quotes from official
report as reproduced in the *Illustrated London News* for
the May 27, 1950).[34] The caption to a photograph of
this rock-shelter reads: "An overhanging cliff in the beech
forest above Notornis (Takahe) Valley where a Maori

hunters' encampment, about 100 years old, was found". That's *circa* 1850 and well into the modern history of New Zealand. But then in *Nature* magazine[35] for March of 1951, we read: "Much of this region has certainly never seen a white man and, probably, not even an old-time Maori. No one knows what wildlife treasures lie hidden within its confines. Great possibilities of discovery await those with a Nature [sic] interest and adventurous inclinations". We seem to be getting a bit muddled here, but perhaps we should not be too hard upon the latter author. All seem to be agreed that there were once Maoris in these mountain fastnesses, that they were hunters in the old traditional manner, that they captured and ate moas, and that they used their bones and feathers for other purposes. Further, there is already good evidence, despite the absence of any definite radiocarbon dating of these bird remains, that this man-bird association continued until the middle of the last century. (At which point one may praise Mr. L. E. Richdale, quoted above from *Nature* Magazine, for the latter part of his pontification.) What indeed may not remain to be discovered there? And this brings up another point.

What happened to the Maoris? Possibly they became extinct due simply to lack of food, particularly during the somewhat rugged winter, though one cannot see why they did not—at the onset of that season—move down from the mountains to the heavily forested and uninhabited lower-reaches by the oceanside where there is plenty of food to gather throughout the winter. Maybe they died out from a disease carried from the lowlands from which they were initially evicted—diseases imported by the *Late Maoris* and/or the white men who carried into the Pacific all manner of horrible diseases. On the other hand some might have survived. Personally, I don't believe in this possibility but there are New Zealanders, of the sort who ought to know what they are spouting, who seriously suggest just this.

If a group of the *Early Maoris* could get along in this southern Fjordland from *circa* 1700 to 1850, as others have stated, why should they suddenly die out? Truly, their original and main source of protein might have been moas but (as stated above) there were obviously many other animals available, and these still exist in considerable numbers—and not only the flightless takahes, kakapos (a kind of parrot), kiwis, and such, but all manner of duck, herons, and others. Also, down by the coast there were fish and many more birds and a really wide variety of vegetable products that were definitely known to the Maoris. Further, these inquisitors point out, these wretched people may not have known how to make fire in the excessively damp climate, or they might simply have lost their transportable "fire" (such as many primitives carry with them when on trek). They would then have had to resort to collecting, hunting, and a diet of raw materials. This is not by any means impossible; in fact, it can be very healthy. Our modern "Survival Manuals" make it quite clear that people initially healthy and devoid of dire endemic disease, can survive very well indeed without fire for cooking. However, the very idea that there might be relic peoples in this area seems more than just exaggerated.

But, if there were people there and they did die out completely, we have to face the real pith of this matter: Did any moas survive? If even the minimum to keep their breed going did survive, they would, on the demise of the Maoris, obviously have had a much better chance of making a comeback. From what has been said by all these most cautious persons it would seem that this might well have happened. Fortunately, as a result of the rediscovery of the Takahe, the government of New Zealand has set aside this enormous area as a reserve and is sending a constant stream of competent, trained scientists and naturalists to explore the area and to truly "conserve" it. If there are any moas left, there is a very good chance that they will be found and, what is more, that the finding will not be hushed up, buried or denied. What is so all-fired important or exciting about getting a rather dismal little flightless elephant-bird may well be open to question. But, there is buried in all of us a certain fascination with the past and—as I said above—it would just be a nice thing to get.

Part II

MORE MAN THINGS

Chapter 5.

WANDERING WOODSPERSONS

IN NOVEMBER 1967, two young men by the name of Roger Patterson and Bob Gimlin turned up in New York with some thirty feet of 16-mm color film of a female "something" that they said they had taken up in the famous Bluff Creek in Del Norte County of northern California the month before. I had heard of this from a correspondent in the area the day after they came out of the woods. I had also corresponded with Roger Patterson for some years on the subject of what they call in Canada the "Sasquatch", and colloquially in Washington, Oregon, and California, "Bigfoot". It was up this same creek that the whole business of giant, fully-haired, ultra-primitive hominids first really got its start in the modern world. A number of very reliable citizens (employed in constructing the first access-road into a vast wilderness area that forms the north portion of the state of California) were constantly visited by "some-things" that left enormous, human-formed, naked footprints, making mile-long tracks night after night around their operations; they had taken plaster casts of these tracks, and in the same area they had found piles of fresh faeces of a human form but of enormous volume.

Subsequent events have made it clear that there are a lot of what one must call "ins-and-outs" to this story, and I therefore feel it best and only fair that I give Patterson's story first, and verbatim from my first interview. This went as follows:[36]

At three-thirty on the twentieth of October (1967) we were packing our horses back into one of the last remaining great wilderness areas, northeast of Eureka, California. Our saddlebags contained on one side rifles and grub and, on the other, ready-loaded movie- and still-cameras and other equipment. We were following a creek which had been washed out two years previously in the terrible floods that devastated most of northern California. This was some twenty miles up the access-road for logging, and about thirty-five miles in from the nearest and only blacktop road in this vast and as-yet-not-fully-mapped area of National Forest. [I have been up this Bluff Creek and, as a botanist, I can tell you that it is rugged—four layers or tiers of trees, the tallest up to two-hundred feet, and a dense undergrowth. Also, the terrain goes up and down like a gigantic sawtooth. *Author.*]

We rounded a sharp bend in the sandy arroyo of the creek. *Then it happened.*

The horses reared suddenly in alarm and threw both of us. Luckily, I fell off to the right and grabbed my camera. Why? Because I had spotted what had turned our horses into mad broncos. About one-hundred feet ahead, on the other side of the creek bed, there was a huge, hairy creature that walked like a man! 'Gosh darn it, Ivan', [he said] 'right there was a Bigfoot. And, fer pity's sakes, it was a female! Just wait till you see the film.'

On the other side of the creek, back up against the trees, there was a sort of man-creature that we estimated later, by measuring some logs that appear in the film, to have been about seven feet tall. Both Bob and I estimate—and this pretty well matched what others told us from examination of the depth to which her tracks sank into hard sand—that she would weigh about three hundred and fifty pounds. She was covered with short, shiny, black hair, even her big droopy breasts. She seemed to have a sort of peak on the back of her head, but whether this was longer hair or not I don't know. Anyhow, hair came right down her forehead to meet her eyebrows, if she had any; and it came right up to just under her cheekbones. And—oh, get this—she had no neck! What I mean is, the bottom of her head just seemed to broaden out onto and into her wide, muscular shoulders. She walked like a big man in no hurry. I don't think you'll see it in the film, but the soles of her feet were definitely light in color." [This last bit got me, as I have seen *really* black-skinned Melanesians with pale pink palms and soles.]

Roger did something then that I have never known any professional photographer to do, even if his camera was loaded with the right film: he had the cap off the lens, and the thing set at the right F stop and so on. He started running, hand-holding his Kodak sixteen-mm, loaded with Kodachrome film, trying to focus on this "creature". What he got was just about what any amateur would get in such circumstances. But then he got a real break. As he puts it:

She was just swinging along as the first part of my film shows but, all of a sudden, she just stopped dead and looked around at me. She wasn't scared a bit. Fact is, I don't think she was scared of *me,* and the only thing I can think of is that the clicking of my camera was new to her."

'Okay', I said, "Tell me this, Roger—the hunting season was on, wasn't it?'

'You're darned-shooting-right it was,' Bob Gimlin chimed in. 'And out that way, anything moving with fur on it is liable to get shot. But actually, there just aren't any hunters way up there, twenty miles beyond the only road. Could it be that this Mrs. Bigfoot knew all about guns but was puzzled by the whirring of a small movie camera? And another thing: everybody who says they have been close to one of these creatures or has found one of their "beds" has stressed the ghastly, nauseating stink they exude and leave behind. Was this what really scared the horses or did the horses scare the thing?'

While Roger took the film, Bob got the horses calmed down and then rode over the creek. Roger was running again after the Bigfoot, still hand-holding his movie camera. Despite the logs and trash on the route she took—and it was not even a game trail—he got some parting shots which turned out to be of particular interest to the scientists. (But we will come to that later.)

At that point, I asked Bob (because he was then what is called "the back-up man," which means that he was now close enough to see Roger clearly) "Just what was Roger doing?"

"He was running like hell, jumping them logs and going up into the real thick bush."

"Did *you* see her, too?"

"Yeah, Ivan, but 'way ahead and really taking off for the hills."

This brought me up sharp, because I had by this time viewed their film (and half a dozen out-takes, blown up, in full color as transparencies, examined under strong magnifying lenses on an illuminated shadow-box several times and projected by three different projectors). In every case, the creature was—at standard speed for photogs, i.e., twenty-four frames per sec—as Roger said, at first just ambling along, swinging her rather long arms, not running-scared, and even stopping for a brief look-see over her shoulder as it were; then ambling on again into the deep woods. Yet here was the back-up man saying that she had "taken off for the hills". Roger, however, backed up his back-up man unprompted:

When she got around the corner and into the real heavy stuff [timber and underbrush] she *did* take off—running, I mean because, when we lost her tracks on pine needles after tracking her for about three and a-half miles, we took plaster casts of her tracks. Now, down by the creek, in the sand, where we first spotted her, her stride was from forty to forty-two inches from the back of the heel on the left side to the back of the right heel ahead; but when she got really going, she left tracks that measured sixty-five inches from back heel to back heel. Man, she was running just like you and I do!

We ran the film again, slowly, and we had a stop-and-hold device on the projector by which you can hold any frame without fear of burning it. This we did and—so help me—there are definitely large, pendant breasts fully covered with short, black hair. No ape (or monkey) is known to have any such development of the female mammary glands. Human beings, on the other hand, do—frequently.

This is the end of the Patterson-Gimlin story, and they have neither added to it nor detracted from it since. Nor, for once, have others attempted to do so, though there has been a great deal of both comment and criticism. This was occasioned by the nature of the story itself, and it is more than worth just mentioning, as a lot that has come to the surface throws new light on this knotty problem. But first, it is probably best to explain what happened after Patterson had his film developed.

To get this done he went to Hollywood where he sensibly had dupes made and then took the original back to Yakima and deposited it in a bank vault. He then tried to get some American scientists to look at it but none would, so he went to British Columbia at the invitation of the two oldest "Sasquatch"-hunters there—John Green, a newspaper publisher, and René Dahinden, originally a Swiss professional mountaineer but for nearly two decades employed by the Canadian Forestry Service. There, a showing was put on for a number of scientists. At this meeting, there were, in addition to Dr. Ian McTaggart-Cowan (Dean of Graduate Studies at the University of British Columbia, and the province's leading zoologist) a dozen or so scientists, including Don Abbott, an anthropologist with the Provincial Museum in Victoria. Most of the scientists admitted in print that, though they had come to the meeting as skeptics, they had left somewhat shaken. Here's how they stated their reactions in the Vancouver *Province* next day:

> Dr. McTaggart-Cowan summed up the more cautious opinions when he said: "The more a thing deviates from the known, the better the proof of its existence must be." Don Abbott spoke for the dozen or more scientists who appeared remarkably close to being convinced: "It is about as hard to believe the film is faked as it is to admit that such a creature really lives. If there's a chance to follow up scientifically, my curiosity is built to the point where I'd want to go along with it. Like most scientists, however, I'm not ready to put my reputation on the line until something concrete shows up—something like bones or a skull." Frank Beebe, well-known Vancouver naturalist and provincial museum illustrator, commented: "I'm not convinced, but I think the film is genuine. And if I were out in the mountains and I saw a thing like this one, I wouldn't shoot it. I'd be too afraid of how human it would look under the fur. From a scientific standpoint, one of the hardest facts to go against is that there is no evidence anywhere in the western hemisphere of primate (ape, monkey) evolution—and the creature in the film is definitely a primate."

Beebe's objection, however, was typical of those given by other experts who ventured out of their own specialties to comment.

Since I know something about primates and about geography, I brought this matter to the attention of Dr. A. Joseph Wraight, Chief Geographer of the U.S. Coast and Geodetic Survey. His full statement appears later but may be summed up here by saying that the distinguished Dr. Wraight—whose doctorate is in Human Ecology—responded in effect, "Bunk!" to this last objection.

A representative of *Life Magazine* was present at this showing and advised his home office that they should review the film. As a result, Patterson and Gimlin were flown to New York where they put on a showing—or rather, let it be shown—to the American Museum of Natural History staff representatives. And here some very shocking performances were initiated. Once again, as in Canada, the press wire-services were on hand but were informed (in closed session, I am told) by these experts that the whole thing was nothing but a colossal hoax, the exact expression used by their spokesman being, as reported to me, "*not kosher*"! The reason alleged to have been given was simply that such a creature as depicted was impossible. The use of this term would, in this case, seem to imply that while considered a hoax, it was short of a fraud; but, if the creature depicted is impossible, then for my money it could only have been a manmade thing and thus an outright fraudulent design. I have failed to receive any suggestions for a third alternative. This is manifestly a most unsatisfactory situation. Furthermore, the verdict pronounced upon the pictures was handed down so fast that no time could have been given for a proper, thorough, and truly scientific examination of them to have been made. Finally, the existence of such a creature is *not* impossible. (I should add that Patterson and his associates were disbarred from the room while the film was run!)

As a result of this, *Life Magazine* washed its hands of the matter and *Argosy Magazine* moved in swiftly. We then went to work to get this film a proper showing before some people who really knew what they were talking about in the field of human physical anthropology, primatology, and pongid and hominid distribution. At the same time, my organization went to work on the other aspect of the problem as we always do—i.e., the human aspects of the case. And this is where things began to come to light; and on both sides of the coin.

First, the film was flown down to Dr. W. C. Osman Hill at the Yerkes Primate Research Center, at Emory University, Atlanta, Georgia. Dr. Hill was the first physical anthropologist to properly investigate the original "abominable snowman" business of the Himalayan region when he was Prosector of the Zoological Society of London. The film was then shown in Washington, D.C. to a distinguished group, including Dr. John R. Napier, also previously of London, now Director of the Primate Biology Program at the Smithsonian Institution, and probably the world's greatest expert on feet and foot-tracks; Dr. Vladimir Markotic, Associate Professor of Archaeology at the University of Calgary, Alberta, Canada; Dr. Allan Bryan, Professor of Anthropology at the University of Alberta, Canada, and also a leading physical anthropologist; Dr. A. Joseph Wraight, Chief Geographer, the U.S. Coast and Geodetic Survey; and Mr. N. O. Wood, Jr., Director of Management Operations for the U.S. Department of the Interior, representing the Honorable Secretary of that department, Stewart Udall, at the latter's specific request. Their expressed opinions were, for the record, as follows:

Dr. Osman Hill: The creature portrayed is a primate and clearly hominid rather than pongid. Its erect attitude in locomotion, the gait, stride and manner of that locomotion, as well as the relative proportions of pelvic to pectoral limb are all manifestly human, together with the great development of the mammary glands. This does not, of course, preclude the possibility that it is indeed a *Homo sapiens* masquerading as a hairy 'giant'. All I can say, at this stage, is that if this was a masquerade, it was extremely well done and effective.

Dr. John R. Napier: I observed nothing that, on scientific grounds, would point conclusively to a hoax. I am satisfied that the walk of the creature shown in the film was consistent with the bipedal striding gait of man (except in the action of the feet, which were not visible). I have two reservations which are both subjective: First, the slow cadence of the walk and the fluidity of the bodily movements, particularly the arms, struck me as exaggerated—almost self-conscious in comparison with modern man; second, my impression was that the subject was male, in spite of the contrary evidence of heavy, pendulous breasts. The bodily proportions of the creature, as far as could be seen, appeared to be within normal limits for man. The appearance of the high crest on top of the skull is unknown in man, but given a creature as heavily built as the subject, such a biomechanical adaptation to an exclusively fibrous raw vegetable diet is not impossible. The presence of this crest, which occurs only in male non-human primates, such as the gorilla and the orangutan, tends to strengthen my belief that this creature is a male. Finally, it might be supposed that a creature with a heavy head, heavy jaw and musculature and a massive upper body would have a center of gravity placed at a higher level than in man. The position of the center of gravity modifies the gait and the easy stride shown in the film is not in harmony with a high center of gravity. The opinions I have expressed on this remarkable film are those of an expert witness, rather than a member of a jury.

Dr. A. Joseph Wraight: The presence of large, hairy humanlike creatures in North and Central America, often referred to as Sasquatch, appears very logical when the physiographic history of the northern part of this continent is considered. The statement often made that monkeylike creatures were never developed in North America may easily be discounted, for these creatures are more humanlike than apelike and they apparently migrated here, rather than representing the product of indigenous evolution. The recent physiographic history of the polar edges of North America reveals that the land migration of these creatures from Asia to America is a distinct and logical possibility. The compelling reason for this distinct possibility is that a land bridge between Asia and North America is known to have existed several times within the last million years, at various intervals during the Pleistocene or Ice Age. The land bridges, both on the north and south sides of the Bering Sea, were admirably suitable for migrations several times during the Ice Age. It appears,

then, that these hairy, humanlike creatures, sometimes called Sasquatch, could easily have migrated to
North America at several times during the Ice Age.
This is particularly plausible when it is considered
that conditions were mild in that area when the land
bridges existed. These creatures could have then
found conditions along the way similar to their Asian
mountain habitat and could naturally have migrated
across the bridges.

During a four-hour session, the films and stills were
shown, examined under high magnification, challenged,
questioned, argued about, and studied. The scientists did
not agree on all points. They did not even all see exactly
the same details in the often hard-to-interpret blowups.
But, after careful scrutiny over a period of hours, not one
of the quoted men voiced the suspicion that there was
even a vague possibility that someone with enormous
funds, and a strange, undecipherable motivation, a disre-
gard for life and limb, and an enormous knowledge of
anatomy, physiology, photography and human psychology *might* have been clever enough to set up a hoax good
enough to fool the *top* experts in their field. And this is a
point that ought to be cleared out of the way first.

This whole case has to be broken down. First, we have
the two opposed aspects, the human aspect (meaning the
background of Patterson, Gimlin, and others involved)
and the scientific aspect. Second, the scientific aspect must
be split into consideration of the hoax—either as deliberately perpetrated by *Messrs*. Patterson and Gimlin, or as
perpetrated *upon* them. This includes analysis of the film
itself, *per se*—meaning, is there any evidence that it was
tampered with afterwards, or even before (as this too can
be done)?

Then, we must ask—*could* this thing be possible? And
here we have to consider the overall picture, i.e., could
there be ultra-primitive hominids in northern California; if
this is a genuine film of one how does it (or does it not)
fit into the known parameters of biological mechanics and
performance? We cannot, as all the scientists pointed out
above, even speculate upon its anatomy or physiology
until we have got a specimen, dead or alive. Thus, we can
deal only with its morphology or external form and its
movements. I will now tackle all of these aspects, *seriatim*.

Certain facts concerning poor Roger Patterson have been brought to light, that might (if taken at face value and without proper investigation) not only look suspicious but cast serious doubt upon the whole matter. None of these facts is incriminating—in that none even alleges any form of criminality—but they are just the sort of nasty hints and even "rumours" that are calculated to make the skeptics and even the "fence-sitters" more readily doubt the whole thing. I have been in investigative work for over thirty years, and on this occasion I had advice from quite a host of specialists both paid and voluntary, and all I can say as of the time of writing (and I would like to say this emphatically) is that not one of these allegations has so far "proved-out," as the saying goes. Roger Patterson was at one time employed in show business, and Bob Gimlin was not available when a film unit went to make a documentary of this affair, and the creature in the film *does* look exactly like a drawing by Mr. Martin Kunsler for an article published by *Sports Afield* in 1960;[37] but none of this, (and more especially the endless little petty-hints that the average human being seems incapable of foregoing) has so far stood up. One person even walked into a publisher's office in New York and stated flatly that he knew who had made the "monkey-suit" and the B-class movies in which it had been used; yet, he could not substantiate one single statement that he had made nor could he give names, dates, addresses or anything else. But none of this is in any way extraordinary: go ask any police officer.

Turning then to the scientific aspects we encounter almost as much nonsense. But on one point all seemed to be agreed. This was that not one of these specialists could find any more evidence than did the Hollywood special-effects and make-up people, that *the film itself* had been tampered with or that the creature it depicted was a phoney. I find this most interesting and significant. They all agreed that in this modern technical day and age almost anything *can* be constructed or "faked". Even in the late 1920s the "dinosaurs" in the film of Conan Doyle's *The Lost World* were utterly realistic—close-ups of their heads showed drooling saliva, nictitating membranes, and flashing eyes. (Incidentally, these "dinosaurs" were wearing skillfully constructed "suits" made by a man who had a degree in palaeontology, and were fitted over live chickens!)

What all these true experts in design, delusion (legitimate) and technology have told me is simply this: "We have been asked if we could make a suit like the one in this film-strip. Our answer is 'Yes'—but given two things: time and a lot of money and a copy of the film to copy from." *This* is the point. Anybody can make a "King Kong", or a gorilla, or a Frankenstein monster provided they know what the producer wants, but they cannot and will not attempt to make a "something" that nobody has previously thought of. In this case, they one and all have pointed out that in view of the way in which the muscles moved *reciprocally under* the skin that they would have had to design a whole new set of muscles, somehow inflatable and controlled by the actor wearing the suit. These muscles would have to be moved in a manner quite different from his own, *and quite differently* from that of a gorilla or a "King Kong." To invent these from a still drawing, such as Kunsler's mentioned above, is difficult even for anatomists with a lifetime knowledge of pongid and hominid musculature and their movements. If then, this film is of a man wearing a "monkey-suit", whoever made it must have had very remarkable knowledge of both ape and human anatomy *and also* that of ABSMs. Just where did he get this?

When one comes to analyze the real possibility of this thing, we encounter something else: Dr. Wraight has answered the first question categorically. There were ultra-primitive hominids in eastern Asia—the *Pithecanthropines,* and especially those once called *Sinanthropus,* in Manchuria—and later the proto-hominids, called collectively *Neanderthalers,* right across Eurasia to eastern Siberia. According to all the anthropologists, archaeologists and even prehistorians the Amerinds came over to the New World via the landbridges spanning the Bering Strait, and the Eskimos came over the same way later. Why shouldn't the earlier, more primitive hunters and gatherers have done likewise?

If the Patterson-Gimlin film *is* a fake it still does not detract one iota from the main problem. These young men were not alive when the "Sasquatch"-Tokimussi-Ohmah- "Bigfoot" business began over a century earlier. (They *could* have had a suit made and they *could* have made the plaster casts of the foot-tracks from casts made by others elsewhere, but the onus of proof lies with those that say they did.) Exactly similar creatures have been reported for over a century all the way from Alaska to Arizona and again from Sinaloa in Mexico to Tierra del Fuego at the southern tip of South America. Further, similar tracks have turned up over all this area for over a century by the tens of thousands, sometimes running for miles in uninhabited and unvisited territory. We have some hairs, and the piles of faeces of human form but of positively vast proportions, composed of local waterweeds and containing worm parasites. The composition of these faeces is like that of indigenous western-Amerindian tribal-groups and that of some men and pigs in *western* China, just exactly where the Sasquatch-type "Hun-guressu" or "Dzu-Teh" with similar feet is found. But then come the really extraordinary objections of the anatomists and certain non-biological technologists. I will deal with the latter first.

Those of the latter principally concerned the lighting of the film and notably the angle of incidence of the shadows. Patterson and Gimlin stated that it was shot at 3:30 p.m. in late October. Several people tried to show that the shadows should have been much more attenuated. However, they predicated this on the fact that Bluff Creek runs *generally* north to south, and they completely overlooked the fact that it constantly twists and turns, and that at the particular point where the film was said to have been shot it ran (around the bend) west to east, so that the shadows were going away from the camera and not across its field of vision; however, this really has nothing to do with the authenticity of the film. The other queries all centered around the matter of the height of the creature depicted. The man best qualified to pronounce on this point, Quentin Keynes, who is among the best and most experienced wildlife photographers alive, came up with exactly the same estimate as Patterson and Gimlin, that the creature was between six and seven feet tall, most probably nearer the latter. I know the exact bend in the creek where this film is alleged to have been shot as I was specifically investigating the vegetation there, and this height-estimate is consistent with the foreground, background, and the nature of the ground.

Turning to the anatomists, we find three principal

queries—the stance, the gait, and the movement of the muscles. To this must be added the most extraordinary contention that the creature is—or looks more like—a male despite the enormous pendant breasts, and particularly because of the funny little peak on the back of its head. The arguments for this latter assumption seem to be purely subjective and, I fancy, due more to preconception than conception. They insist that no female primates have such back-of-head topnotches, and that no male hominid has it either. This is just not so, since many known monkeys (both the New and Old World ones), the gorilla among the apes, and an endless parade of humans even today have veritable crests and *at the back* of their heads, as exemplified by certain Capuchins in South America, some Mangabeys and Guenons in Africa, several Langurs of the Orient and African women of many tribes. These crests or peaks are composed solely of hair; certain pongids like the male gorilla also have a bony crest called a sagittal ridge to which very large masseter muscles—which pull up the lower jaw in order to crack, crunch, and chew rough, hard vegetable food—are attached.

There is then a corollary argument put forward about the head of the thing as shown in this film. The anatomists tell us that if there is such a sagittal bony crest, the lower jaw or mandible would have to be very deep. This too is unfortunately not the case. This may be seen in all the bone-crackers (like hyaenas) and the great cats which have very slender lower jaws, just as do the carnivorous reptiles, both living and fossil. The objection to the crest and the jaw just doesn't hold water. Nor does the matter of gait.

If the torso or upper part of a creature that stands and walks on its two back legs is larger and heavier than the lower part, it would have to tilt or lean forward simply to get going. The ultimate of this upper-body to lower-body bulk is the male gorilla which cannot go forward at all unless it props its top- or front-end up on its long arms. The animal in the Patterson film leans forward just the right amount for its proportions. Its arms are long, but not excessively so, in proportion to the length of its legs. Likewise with its gait—it "swings" along with a very free and fluid motion.

It is very hard to comment on the movement of the muscles because no two real experts seem to agree just how they do move, both directly or reciprocally. From viewing the film, they look very "natural" to me, and I say this as one who has spent over forty years observing animals (and especially primates) in the wild and in captivity—but the naturalness could just as well be that of a very heavy-set human. After all, we are only animals, and primates at that, and even very closely related to the pongids. In my opinion the rippling and smoothly flowing muscles as shown in the film do not look artificial but, as I have said above, they *could* be.

This ends the queries of the anatomists, and I am afraid I have to say that not only do they not stand up on any one count, they are unfortunately just those points most vulnerable to refutation. Only Napier's "feeling" or impression that the thing was male impresses me. Curious indeed—and probably quite unscientific—to say this, since impressions have no place in scientific analysis—but how often has this sort of "feeling" for reality advanced knowledge when all the computers and laboratory bottles have gotten nowhere. And then comes another impressionist, the only morphologist so far, with vast experience and training, and one who has applied modern statistical (computer-type) analysis to just such a problem as this—Dr. Bernard Heuvelmans. His comments are as follows:

In all furry animals the hair has a definite pattern, that is, on each area of the body the hairs are oriented in a certain direction. For instance, on a chimpanzee's arm, or even on a man's if he is hairy, they go down from the shoulder to the elbow, and up from the wrist to the elbow. This definite hair pattern can be seen even on photographs of animals from the way the light shines on their fur.

On the creature shown on Patterson's film there is nothing of the sort. As can be seen from the way the hairs shine, giving the fur a speckled appearance, they point in all directions (compare the blowups of the film with photographs of gorillas or, better, of certain bears, which have 'short, shiny, black hair', and you will see that in the latter, the shine on the fur shows that on each part of the body the hairs all point in the same direction.

The aspect of the hair of the creature in the film is exactly what should be expected from artificial fur—

whether thick velvet or nylon fur—in which all threads (not actually hairs) are attached uniformly on some canvas base. When you stroke this material in different directions, the artificial hairs get bent in these directions and remain so until you brush them all carefully in the same direction.

Patterson adds—which is also seen in the film—that 'even her big, droopy breasts' are covered with short, shiny black hair. This would of course be possible in some unknown species of man, but it would be rather improbable to say the least. In all larger apes the breasts have a slight tendency toward swelling, and even dropping a little, when the female is nursing its baby or if it has been nursing many of them, but even in such hairy primates the chest is almost naked.

I want to add that this (to me) obvious hoax does not shake at all my firm conviction that some large unknown human-like primate lives in the northwest of the United States and in the western provinces of Canada, not to mention of course certain mountain ranges of northeastern and central Asia."

This sums up this extraordinary case as of the time of writing. Nothing has been proved and nothing has been disproved, despite all the sound and some considerable fury. But this is par for the course in these matters. All we can hope for is the capture of an ABSM in the area, which would settle one rankling question. However, even that would probably not solve the second one—to wit, was this film a fraud?

Chapter 6.

GIANT SKULLS

THERE ARE SOME THINGS I can readily accept; there are others, however, over which I boggle, or from which I retreat precipitately. I have been in full retreat from this one for nearly eight years, but I am afraid that, on the grounds of common honesty, I must now throw all caution to the proverbial winds—i.e., the storm of criticism—and give it to you straight. This whole business at first sounds so balmy as to constitute an absurdity ... but. ...

The possibility of there being a number of different large or as-yet-uncaught and unidentified *animals* existing in the seas and oceans does not faze me one bit. In fact, since we have a film of something of this nature in a fresh-water lake (see Tim Dinsdale's effort on the Loch Ness Monster)[38] I am prepared to say that the possibility has moved up into the category of probability. I long ago accepted that it was highly probable that there were large primitive human beings clothed in fur, still existing in many parts of the world, including our own Northwest.[39] We now have a film of such an alleged creature taken by a Mr. Roger Patterson of Yakima, Washington, that has been viewed by a group of Canadian scientists and pronounced by them to be not a fake and definitely to constitute the next stage toward accepting the existence of such creatures. But when it comes to this one... !

I will not forget the day that a man, who had collected oddities for many years, came to me in New York with samplings of his massive files, dumping on my desk a fat item on the subject of such hairy primates as reported from British Columbia, Washington, Oregon, and northern California. Frankly, although I had for years been collecting material on the infamous "abominable snowman", "Meh-teh", or *Yeti* of the Himalayas and was agreeable to accepting the reports on it from European and American mountaineers, I was just not prepared for the same or similar things right in our own back yard. But then, ten years later I went to that "back yard" and saw for myself the endless parade of foot-tracks left by such alleged creatures, and talked with hundreds of the sanest local folk who stated that they had known of these creatures since childhood and who alleged, in many cases, that they had encountered them themselves. But enough of what we *do* know and which some of us have accepted. This up-coming item is, I must say in all honesty, just a bit too much.

Gigantic—not just "giant"—human beings living in the sea! But first, the facts (or allegations), then some analysis, and, finally, some "history".

In 1961 I wrote a book entitled *Abominable Snowmen— Legend Come to Life*, which covered just about all that has been said on the matter of relic, primitive, fully-furred hominids still existing in various parts of the world from Scandinavia and the Caucasus, throughout the mountainous areas of Asia, to Siberia, then into Alaska, and south all the way down the western sides of North, Central, and South America to Tierra del Fuego, as well as all across northern Canada, and in various places in the tropics. As a result, all manner of interesting little ditties came to me in the mail. Most of them simply confirmed what I had said other people had said about these things, or added similar items, but from other areas. Among them, however, was a remarkable letter from a lady in Idaho—remarkable not only for the information it contained but also for its extraordinary cogency and the manifest demonstration that the writer was a person of not only higher education, but of rather exceptional erudition. Among other things (after denigrating herself almost to the point of near intellectual extinction) she announced that she had just published a book on the hybridization of Irises. You don't, or cannot, do that unless you know something of genetics. I would like to publish this letter in full, but space does not allow, so I must paraphrase.

The facts came from one of her sons (she was a great-grandmother) who had been an engineer in the U.S. Army during World War II. This man relates the following:

Having volunteered in 1940 for active duty, he was sent to join an engineering unit that built the Alcan Highway to Alaska. When this was completed, he was sent, with this unit, the 1081st Company, Maintenance Engineers, to the island of Kodiak for a rest period, and was then shipped with his unit to a tiny island named Shemya that lies half a mile east of Attu (and which is separated from it only by a half-mile shallow channel) that is the last of the Aleutians going towards Asia. The Japanese were still on Attu and the purpose of landing on Shemya was to turn the island into an airstrip, it being flat and low, except for a small rise at the eastern end. Enemy resistance had been expected here but, on landing, only one dead Japanese soldier was found. However, there were neat signs all around the island stating that it, and anything found on it, was the property of (*of all things*) the Smithsonian Institution! When these signs were erected was not known to this engineering outfit—whether they were pre-war and left by the Japanese, erected by the enemy, or by some military unit that had got there before them. This business is odd to say the least; but wait.

According to my correspondent, her son stated that when the bulldozers arrived, they started leveling the whole island of small bumps and finally tackled the slight elevation at the east end. Curiously, this was said to have been composed of many layers of "muck", silt, and soil, with underlying *sedimentary* rock, while the lower land and the beaches were composed of a mixture of sedimentary and non-sedimentary rocks and boulders. As this eastern bump was scooped off, bones of all kinds began to come to light; first, those of whales, seals, walrus and such, but later and lower, those of extinct animals like mammoths. Finally, at a depth of about six feet, what appeared to be a graveyard of *human remains* was uncovered. These were wholly of crania (not whole skulls) and the long bones of the legs. Associated with them were numerous doll-like artifacts carved out of mammoth and walrus ivory, but "fossilized"—*after* they had been carved. There were also chipped flint instruments (no flint on the island) and other bone and stone implements of both very small and a rather large size.

The crania of the human skulls, which are categorically stated to be of modern human conformation with full foreheads (not sloping, ape-like ones with big browridges) *measured from 22" to 24" from base to crown*. What is more, every one of them is said to have been neatly trepanned!

Now, the average person's skull measures only about 8" from front to back, and the cranium, i.e., the upper bit containing the brain box, stands only about 6" high—and we measure an average 5 feet 6 inches tall. Of course, there can be small people with very big heads, and there can be enormous people with small heads. I once crossed the Pacific on a Japanese liner with a Texan who was then *alleged* to be the tallest man in the world, at 9'2" in height. Of course, he wore a 100-gallon hat, so that the size of his head could not be accurately ascertained. He also wore cowboy boots, but he was indeed impressive, and had to enter the main saloon on all fours. He was also a charmer, especially to the Japanese stewardesses who did not reach his waist, and the Captain who did—just. However, the proportions of the body to the head in the case of a cranium that stands nearly two feet tall are something quite else again. Such an enormity is this, that we resorted to some practical investigation by blowing up the outline of a modern-type human skull, enlarged to the measurements given, but on the conservative side of 22″ high. The proportions and size of the body needed to support this item—of a humanoid form—would be something that stood about twenty feet.

Now, a large male giraffe may stand almost twenty feet, and the extinct *Baluchitherium*, the bulkiest land animal we know—the dinosaurs not excluded—which was related to the rhinoceroses, also stood as tall and had a gigantic and massive body. However, both these animals are supported on four legs. A humanoid of this type would presumably stand on only two, and, while its bulk would be less than that of either of these other animals, gravity would still exert an enormous pull (or push) down upon these two legs. How could the creature get about, even with enormous leg muscles? There is a limit to the tonnage that bone can support on the surface of this earth (in air that is) and, although bone is an amazingly strong material, it has to become progressively more massive to support weights above a certain point; and there would seem to be a point beyond which it simply cannot go, lest it become so massive that it literally bogs down the whole animal. But in water . . .

The record whale ever measured was a female Blue at 113½ feet; and by the new method of estimating total weight at 1½ tons per foot of length, this comes out at about 170 tons. This enormity probably could, like its *confreres*, leap clean out of the sea, but if stranded it would die of suffocation in short order, since its sheer weight would crush the rib-cage and lungs. Buoyed up by water, however, the gravitational pull on its mass was completely nullified. The same goes for all other animals that live in water—fifty-foot squids, one-ton jellyfish, six-foot lobsters, and so on.

Now, if we must accept this report of human-like beings with crania 22″ high, and thus needing a massive body some twenty feet tall to support them, what would be the most rational solution of their problem? It would be for them to live in or spend most of their time in water.

There are two aspects to this mad exercise. First, a highly esteemed scientist of the utmost probity, Professor

Alister Hardy of Oxford University, England, made so bold as to publish a technical paper in 1960 on the possibility that (modern) man went through a semi-aquatic stage by gaining his food by diving for shellfish off shallow coasts.[40] A note in this paper suggested that he (man) had retained head-hair to protect his scalp from the sun. This notion at first sounds almost as balmy as our present exercise, but this scientist was neither ridiculed nor read out of court. In fact, he was taken seriously by many of his colleagues (this is something that has never ceased to amaze me). The other aspect of the suggestion that, if twenty foot men ever did exist, they must have lived in the sea, and this leads us into other channels. We will start with the word "kelp".

This word is defined by the dictionary as: "Large kinds of seaweed; calcined ashes of same, used for the manufacture of carbonate of soda, iodine, etc., formerly used in making soap and glass". "Kelpie", on the other hand, is a Gaelic word now incorporated into the English language, but meaning originally a "Water-Spirit, usually in the form of a horse, reputed to delight in the drowning of travelers, etc." (Note the somewhat ominous "etc.".) From the former designation we derive our North American name for the vast beds of seaweed that grow in comparatively shallow waters all along our west coast from the farthest western Aleutian Islands, via Alaska, to southern California, which local citizens call simply the "kelp beds". These are very remarkable in many respects, not the least being that some of their vast fronds that float at the surface of the sea are anchored to the bottom by stalks that may be nearly half a mile long. In these kelp beds there exists a large and varied fauna; these range from specialized invertebrates that cling or buzz about in its floating fronds to the Gray Whale, several seals and sealions, and the remarkable Sea-Otter. Most of these animals are predaceous or carnivorous, and they find a wealth of food in the kelp beds.

A race of twenty-foot-tall humans could not obtain however, even in this environment, enough animal food to maintain themselves. Lacking the cutting-teeth of the seals, or the scoop-mouths of whales which ingest tons of small food, or grasping appendages, they just would not have been able to gain a living. If, on the other hand, they were vegetarians and fed principally on the kelp itself, they could indeed have thrived and multiplied, and grown to such monumental proportions. Then there is another thing.

There is now undeniable evidence that, whatever the cause—the earth's crust is shifting; the axis wobbling, or the whole earth is going through successive cold and warm phases—the far northern latitudes around the Bering Sea, Alaska, and eastern Siberia once, and until comparatively recently, enjoyed a warm temperate climate. On Wrangel and other islands north of eastern Siberia there have been found, in addition to endless bones of mammoths and other mammals, whole flowering and fruit-bearing trees, notably of the order of the plums, up to forty-feet in length, buried shallowly in the *muck* around their coasts. This whole area in fact seems to have been habitable for a long time by animals evolved in warm temperate climates. Could humanoids, hominids, or even humans have developed the practice—as mooted by Professor Hardy—of gaining their living by diving in moderately warm coastal seas? Could they have continued to do so, while the general climate deteriorated, by leaning most heavily on kelp for food? The idea is admittedly most highly *improbable* but can we honestly say that it is *impossible*?

So, one has to turn to the third and last aspect of this whole preposterous business. This is to say, to the "historical".

When the lady in Idaho wrote me those four pages of most sensible material, I immediately replied, asking for further information. She replied, saying that her son positively refused to write on this matter and for several reasons: notably that an Englishman (whose name is very well known in the literary field) had annoyed him to the point of complete withdrawal by writing demanding letters of a patronizing nature that infuriated him. However, my correspondent wrote to her son on my behalf and obtained the name and number of the military outfit in which he worked in Alaska, the Yukon, on Kodiak, and on the island of Shemya. I then began a process of checking, working through the General Services Administration, National Personnel Records Center, St. Louis, Missouri.

From this most estimable and competent organization, I obtained the names of four officers of this 1081st Company, including that of their senior Intelligence Officer. I began writing letters. I received most gratifying replies from two of these gentlemen, one who confirmed that he was with the outfit on Shemya but stating that he had not heard of any anthropological or archaeological discoveries there. The other letter, from a gentleman now resident in New Jersey stated: "I recall that as we were building a road around the south east end of Shemya Island, the bulldozers did uncover some human bones, ivory carvings, etc. There was considerable excitement over this. . . . I recall that this area was put under the control of the Base Commander and all of the findings were to be handled by this base unit." The other two retired officers to whom I wrote did not reply. Later, however, I traced down the Senior Intelligence Officer of this unit, but my letter to him was returned, stamped "Moved—No Forwarding Address".

To go back, though, I find that I should report some much less pleasant implications. First, there is this curious business of the island being clearly marked "off-limits" as being the perquisite of the Smithsonian. I do not quite understand this. But then comes a much less pleasant conundrum. It is alleged by my primary informants that the men aboard the island made a sort of hobby of collecting the artifacts found with the bones, but that they were told to turn them all in, under penalty. However, one man who had been a museum preparator, knowing something of their value and possible significance, made a small collection which he hoped to take back to the mainland. This was discovered, and the man was immediately arrested and held *incommunicado*. Later, when a civilian crew of engineers came to relieve the enlisted outfit, this man was allegedly shipped back to the States "in irons", as the saying goes, and was despatched to (the military) Leavenworth.

Then come a number of flat statements from various sources; to wit, that a number of these skulls, or bits of them, plus other bones, some of the "dolls", and other artifacts, were collected, crated, and despatched to the Smithsonian. I have no evidence that this was (or is) so, apart from these written statements. However, now thoroughly irked by all this, I made formal application to the Smithsonian for some clarification of all this—either a written denial of it, or some information as to just what happened to any material of this nature that was shipped to them from the Island of Shemya, *circa* 1945-46. I have never received a reply.

Either this whole story (and I would emphasize that it is just *that,* rather than a "report", as of now) is pure hog-wash, or it is true. If the former, how come such very sensible-sounding persons have written as they have; and how is it that there is confirmation, up to a point, from ex-military personnel who were at the spot when this happened? If it is true, then where the hell are the finds? Why have they not been examined, published upon, and otherwise made public? As my original informant said in one of her letters: "Perhaps you are right in saying that these people just cannot face rewriting all their textbooks."

But the really unpleasant thing to me is being asked to accept anything so utterly bizarre as twenty-foot, semi-aquatic, marine, "modern" humans. Isn't this pushing things a bit too far: or is it? I have to await expressions from the Smithsonian if there are any, which I am afraid I have to say that I rather doubt at this juncture.

Meantime, we reconstructed the outline of the alleged Shemya crania. This was done simply by extrapolation or "blowing-up" the outline of an average modern human cranium. I then asked an old friend of mine, the anthropologist Professor George A. Agogino, currently head of the Paleo-Indian Institute, Eastern New Mexico University, Portales, N. M., to come take a look at the photo. He is one of the very few professional scientists who we felt would not burst out laughing and then refuse even to listen to the story. In this we were correct.

George Agogino said nothing when he first saw this monstrosity. He regarded it for a very long time; then asked if he could go into another room and read the file undisturbed. This he did; when he rejoined us, the first thing he asked was what the shaded outline was within the last molar tooth. I had not pointed this out to him earlier as I wanted him to have the story straight and without this entirely extraneous interjection.

This sort of "inner tooth" in the drawing is an outline-tracing (*actual* size) taken from a photograph of the first tooth of an extinct creature, named *Gigantopithecus,* originally found in a Chinese apothecary store in Hong-Kong by one Dr. G. H. R. von Koenigswald[41] in 1935. (Since then quite a number of teeth and some bones of this giant anthropoid have been found in caves along with other deposits in southern China.) From the conformation of the teeth and bones it is now generally thought that this creature was a giant Pongid or ape. Reconstructions of it have been published, notably one in the *Illustrated London News*.[42] The animal was assessed at eight to twelve feet tall by the British, ten to fifteen feet tall by the Chinese.

Reducing the outline of the cranium to fit this inner *outline*, we then found that we had a skull of such enormous size as to be quite beyond belief. Since this tooth exists, there can be no question about *its* size *per se*. (The alternative is that the creature it grew in had a jaw out of all proportion to the rest of its head, like a *Pithecanthropine*, an *Australopithecine*, or some lower type, or like the crazy Olduvai skull turned up by Leakey.) However, its owner can *not* be a vast ape because this tooth is typically hominid, and even "human" shaped!

We then tried the whole thing over again with a molar tooth of another extinct hominid named *Meganthropus* (thought to be a large form of *Pithecanthropine*) and therefore to have had a very small brain box in proportion to its jaws; but still the skull, patterned on a blowup of *Pithecanthropus* itself, was so enormous it would have required indeed a twelve-foot body to support it. Thus, we found ourselves going around in a circle of speculation. George Agogino was gracious enough to hear us out and comment on each of these efforts without either lapsing into ribaldry or bypassing the "logic" of the exercise. But he did admit to being greatly puzzled by one thing. This was that nobody seemed previously to have "speculated" upon the implications of the sizes of the teeth of *Gigantopithecus* and *Meganthropus*.

Just what kind and size of skull *did* they grow in? Further, did the hominids develop huge vegetarian forms that needed these enormous teeth for crushing rough fibers? Finally, could any such forms have had truly "modern" human-type skulls? There are no answers to these questions, and there will not be until and unless we get substantial parts of said skulls, and of the limb and other bones of the bodies that supported them. Meantime, the results of this speculation throw a rather different light on the Shemya story.

Chapter 7.

WALKERS FOR WATER

THE FULL TITLE of this observation is "He make he do go for walk for water". There is nothing blasphemous in so titling the piece, and no discourtesy to my West African friends is to be implied by the use of this old-fashioned form of what is called pidgin-English; but that jargon is just too delicious to be divorced from this equally "delicious" subject. While this is really a very serious matter, everything in West Africa somehow must have a somewhat humorous aspect.

I have waited for many years now for confirmation of my faith in those who told me of this extraordinary matter and to receive further confirmation of the matter itself for I have had neither the means nor the opportunity "to make me do go, look'um, bring'em, fetch'em, come", which means simply, go and get the damned thing myself. Since I do have faith in those who told me of the business I still, after more than thirty years, hope to hear more. But this is not the kind of thing that many people like to talk about, since very few non-Africans can have an opportunity of witnessing it, and the Africans rather sensibly won't talk at all. I should explain that walking "for water" does not mean walking "on it". To the contrary, in pidgin-English it normally means walking "toward" or "to" water, and this is just what my first informant told me he at first thought the man meant.

The first case was related to me by a Mr. N. H. Cleverley when he held the position of Resident of the Southern British Cameroon back in 1932. Resident was a high office more equivalent to a Chief Justice than a straight political officer. His headquarters were in the town of Calabar at the mouth of the Cross River which enters the Bight of Benin right in the corner of the great bay of the west coast of Africa. His district slopped-over into southern Nigeria on the other side of the river and covered a vast area of swamp and "firmland" forest with a fair-sized population of Sobo, Ibo, and related Sudanese peoples on the Nigerian side, and Anyangs, Akpaboyo and other Bantus on the Cameroon side. Right across the river was the flat, lowland, coastal country of the Ibibio, densely forested and veined with a mazelike network of creeks and rivers.

One day a sergeant of the Native Bush Police came from Ibibio country to the Residence in Calabar and reported that some villages would not pay their taxes and had been rather unpleasant. Nigeria was never a British Colony; it was a Protectorate and under what was called Native Administration. This meant that the people governed themselves under their own laws (with certain emendations such as prohibitions on slaving, ritual genocide, and such, imposed by the British) and collected their own taxes, percentages of which were made over to the next authority above, and so on up the line to central authority. But while Districts (and within them tribal groups, and within these villages) were virtually autonomous, there was cohesion through the law, the army (a militia then) and such organizations as Bush Police, Court Messengers, and such like, while white political officers administered the Districts.

In the case of tax complaints, litigants appealed to the nearest court and tax collectors did likewise. Each District had a court under the aegis of the District Officer, but in the case of a regional capital like Calabar there was one court presided over by the Resident. Thus, this sergeant reported direct to Calabar and the Resident in this case. What he reported and what happened subsequently was on record at that court when I was in the country.

As a result of the complaint lodged by the sergeant, the Resident instructed the District Officer to investigate, and being a very busy man he delegated the matter to one of his Assistant District Officers—who, in turn, passed it on to a cadet. This last personage, poor fellow, would be a new recruit to the Colonial Political Service and was probably on his first tour of duty. Guided by the native sergeant he set off in a paddled canoe through the maze of the Ibibio swamps where anybody short of a locally-bred policeman would get hopelessly lost. In due course, it appears from the record, they landed and walked through dense bush to the main village of the recalcitrant group. It was completely deserted, even by the ubiquitous dogs and some pet monkeys that the sergeant had noticed on his last visit.

They had only two carriers with them as they had intended to return to the great canoe, and they had been very silent on the march over the soft loam of the forest floor. Annoyed and somewhat mystified, the party then moved on to one of the smaller satellite villages, but it also was completely deserted. So were two others and some isolated farmsteads. Now, this group of villages was really on a fairly small island completely surrounded by creeks. All travel in that country is by water and paths exist only to go from little landing-beaches to the center of these islands where the main villages are situated—a legacy from the old days of slave-raiding. There are usually a number of such paths radiating from the center.

Since the villages were deserted, the white officer thought that everybody had pushed off by canoe, assuming that "authority" would eventually descend upon them over the tax palaver, and so he decided to send all his crew into the village by one path, then have them fan out to the creek-beaches in all directions. Meantime, he was to circumnavigate the island in the hope of catching some of the culprits. This campaign was put into action but did not come out as expected in any way, for to their amazement all the beaches were loaded with canoes. Furthermore, the sergeant did a careful count and found that from his personal knowledge only one small canoe was missing! Very frustrated, the sergeant offered to "beat" the whole little island and flush-out the inhabitants that the officer felt sure were hiding in the bush. Permission was granted, but not a soul was found. Now very annoyed, for he was an old-hand and had a new white officer on his hands, the sergeant's pride must have been very hurt for he asked for permission to take a small canoe for the night and go off alone. Apparently he also got permission to doff his uniform and adopt a native cloth.

It later transpired that his original intention had been to go to the nearest adjacent village and make enquiries, but he happened to meet some people returning to the abandoned village from a long trip. They at first said they did not know of the happenings at home, although this was very unusual since Africans always keep in close touch with home via drums when they are in the bush. The sergeant was suspicious and forthwith accused them of having been smuggling. The result was salutary.

The locals collapsed when he further informed them that he was a police officer, and they struck a bargain with him. Yes, they said, they knew where their people were even if they did not know until then the reason for their going there. The sergeant apparently said "lead on" and, being a very typical example of his respected Service, he kept his mouth shut about the presence of the white officer. On getting back to their own island, the men led the sergeant down a very slight trail to one of the creeks, where there were no canoes or a landing-beach. Instead, there was a six-foot, slightly overhanging bank. This creek was a clear-water one (the water ran the color of light sherry rather than the usual turgid, puce-colored soup of the average lowland waters) and the trees on either bank almost met over the top. The locals indicated to the sergeant that he should lean over the bank and look down.

(An interesting aside is that the sergeant's training came to the fore at that point for he dutifully recorded tying the men to a tree first so that they could not push him in and drown him!) Then he peered over. Under examination at a later hearing he insisted, and categorically, that he was not surprised at what he saw because he was an Ibibio himself. This may be so, but nobody except the young white cadet ever really believed him—or what he himself later affirmed they had seen; namely, the entire community of all the villages (over a hundred souls, men, women and children, *and* their pets, which were confined in openwork baskets and appeared to be asleep) sitting motionless at the bottom of the water with their backs to the bank.

That sergeant was a clever man for by the exercise of some infinite diplomacy he persuaded his captives to go with him to the village to discuss the matter. (Personally, I suspect that this was actually a small matter of, let us say, pecuniary adjustment.) He marched them straight into the arms of the officer, had them tied up again, and put under the loving care of the two court messengers who had accompanied the tour. Then he led the cadet back to the creek on the double.

What happened then is the oddest of all. Apparently

the people were about eight feet down, so the officer instructed the sergeant to go down and "wake them up" (as I distinctly remember the phrase). However, that stalwart said it would be impossible. Instead of asking why, the greenhorn must have suspected insubordination and ordered the sergeant to go down instantly—and that worthy did. The white man then confesses to having been greatly disturbed when he saw the sergeant shaking the people violently and trying to push them out into the gentle stream. None "woke up" and all were attached by "tie-tie"—i.e., liana or vine—ropes to tree roots under the bank!

At this point, the young man seems to have rather lost his head because he still did not seek advice of his sergeant, nor did he go down himself to confirm matters. (Personally, I just cannot imagine such an omission but then I have an inexorably inquisitive mind.) Instead, he appears to have charged-off back to his canoe and, leaving the sergeant and the court messengers in charge, high-tailed it back to Calabar. It should be made quite clear that no cowardice is implied by this precipitate action; rather, it seems to have been overly-strict adherence to the instruction manual. He was apparently hell-bent on reporting to his superiors and we must give him full credit for his intention, because it is possible he wanted to have another white man confirm his report. This, however, may not have been quite the praiseworthy objective it appears, for the poor young man was probably wondering what he *was* going to report and just what his reception would be if he told the plain truth with only his native staff to back him up—and he a greenhorn. He need not have worried, because his superiors were "Old Coasters", and after a few tours of duty in West Africa even the dumbest Englishman admits to himself that there is a lot he doesn't know, a lot that is normally considered impossible that nonetheless happens, and that Africa still lives up to its good old Latin password of "*Semper aliquid de novis ex Africa*".

Apparently the report was not received unkindly, for there it is recorded that he returned, accompanied by an Assistant District Officer and others. Strangely, there is no mention of a doctor having gone along. One would have thought that he would have been the most logical officer to investigate such a bizarre allegation of abnormal human behaviour. There was a lot more to the report, but the gist of it was that by the time the white men got there, the sergeant had the whole community back to work and the taxes collected. (From this, one infers that the cadet did not instruct him to keep the people below water till he got back or, alternatively, the sergeant disobeyed orders.) On the other hand the people may have come out of their own accord when the white man left, either on signal from their *confreres* held ashore by the police, or by some more startling means of their own, by which they knew just when the major menace had departed. My informant got rather vague after this, and as the whole thing was a new one to me in those days I don't remember asking him any of the obvious questions—notably, if anybody had ever tried to find out *how* they did it. He was a legal man and was interested primarily in the truth of the whole story, and of this he was apparently firmly convinced.

I was young and I am afraid rather naive in those days and, frankly, I was *not* convinced. [Oh, what an appalling thing youth is, and how much time do we all waste with it. I have often wished for inverse time so that one could be born with a lifetime of experience built in, and so not miss the many opportunities.] In fact, I plain forgot the whole business for about fifteen years but then I got a real jolt.

This was administered to me by an old friend, Geoffrey Gorer, a leading sociologist, and a most extraordinary man whose life reads almost like science-fiction. Geoffrey was always an iconoclast but he has the energy of a House Sparrow and the pertinacity of a groundhog; also he was always as inquisitive as a racoon. Should he ever read this, I hope that he will forgive me for saying that I just don't believe that he is even now sufficiently overawed by orthodoxy to mind my relating the following.

Geoffrey made a trip to Senegal on the West African coast in company with a native of that country who was teaching dancing and studying music in Paris, where Geoffrey was then residing. One day this African friend announced that he wanted to show Geoffrey a rather notable local custom or practice. He was then taken to sea in a small boat to watch some local fishing operations, in absolutely clear water, close inshore and behind a reef.

There were lots of little boats bobbing about and the fishermen were hauling baskets of bottom-living shellfish up to the surface at a steady clip. The visitor(s) were taken alongside and asked to look down, and there was a small army of locals wandering about on the bottom picking the shellfish off the sand and tossing them into baskets just as we would pick strawberries. There was something about their having stones tied to their ankles to keep them down, and they were said to have stayed below for periods of half an hour, or as long as they liked! Geoffrey timed one man at forty-five minutes. I have a vague memory of having been told by somebody else that a white man had been taught how to do this by the locals and had stayed down a great deal longer than even the record for holding one's breath under water—which was achieved, incidentally, by Robert Foster, an electronics technician, who stayed under ten feet of water in a swimming pool at San Rafael, California, for an incredible 13 minutes—42.5 seconds on March 15, 1959. He hyperventilated with oxygen for thirty minutes before his descent.

The length of time that human beings have been alleged to have stayed under water is fraught with the most extraordinary claims. Some are modern and purport to be observations made under controlled conditions; others are historic. Perhaps the most extraordinary of all is that of a professional Sicilian diver of the twelfth century who was nicknamed "Nicolas The Fish". I am indebted to my old friend and colleague, Dr. Bernard Heuvelmans, for permission to reproduce the following summary of this character's history, taken verbatim from his book *Dans le Sillage des Monstres Marins*:[43]

> He was a Sicilian diver of the twelfth century, by the name of Nicolas, whose extraordinary swimming abilities made him deserve the nickname of Nicolas-the-Fish.* His fame must have been considerable, for many authors of the Middle Ages spoke of him, though with sundry variations.

---

*Or *Nicolas Pesce* (Walter Mapes), *Pescecola* (Father Athanasius Kircher), *Colas Poisson* (Father Georges Fournier), or even the Fish Nicolas (Cervantes).

According to Walter Mapes, an Englishman who lived in Italy for a long time toward the end of the twelfth century, this man lived so habitually in the sea that finally he unveiled all its secrets and was able to predict storms. He is said to have died after he had to part from his new environment when he was taken to the King of the Two Sicilies, William the First, who reigned from 1154 to 1166.

Needless to say, as time passed, imaginative commentators began to attribute to this diver of undoubtedly exceptional endurance, some feats impossible to perform without a diver's suit, such as being able to stay under water for three-quarters of an hour! In the seventeenth century the Jesuit scholar, Father Athanasius Kircher, did not hesitate to write that *Pescecola* sometimes lived in the sea for four or five days and that he could stay under water for a whole day without coming to the surface to breathe. Moreover, some authors went so far as to report that he had eventually acquired webbed hands and feet (Kircher), and even fish scales (Jovianus Pontanus, in the fifteenth century).

One of Nicolas's greatest feats is said by Gervase of Tilbury to have been the exploration of Scylla's whirlpool, performed at the order of King Roger of Sicily (probably Roger the Second, who reigned from 1101 to 1154). According to Father Kircher, it was King Frederick the Second (who reigned from 1355 to 1377!) who enticed our hero to dive into Charybde's whirlpool by throwing a gold cup into it. This is obviously an error. If the feats of the celebrated diver have been assigned to very different ages, it is nevertheless probable that a very spectacular sports record is the origin of all these legends."

There was only one further aspect to this report and this I remember well for by that time I was a little more knowledgeable, and I fired a lot of questions at Geoffrey. The only question to which I got a satisfactory answer as to how it was done, was something about a "drug". Personally I am becoming increasingly suspicious of this term and the notion that it "sort of" explains everything. Just because we have produced some almost uncanny effects with drugs and it is now irrefutable that *curand-*

eros, shamans, medicine-men and *juju*-men, and just plain old witch-doctors have for centuries used other often more potent and mysterious herbal derivatives, there seems no excuse for the tendency to use this explanation like a magic wand. Yet admittedly, the notion is not entirely irresponsible in this case, while one must admit to being hard put to it to suggest any alternative. This is especially so in the latter case since the people were *active* while under water—or, I should say, are alleged to have been so.

You may have seen some photographs recently published of pretty little hamsters, apparently quite happily snuffling-about at the bottom of a fish-tank full of water. This and quite a lot of other experiments have now shown that small mammals can live under water for unexpectedly long periods of time considering they are devised to breathe oxygen dissolved in air or other gases, *not* in a liquid. There are various approaches to these experiments, such as enhancing the free oxygen content of the water, altering the metabolic processes of the animal, and so forth. In some of these experiments "drugs" (in the wider sense) have been mentioned. The results obtained were shocking in a way, because they seemed to defy the norm, but most people more or less dismissed them as being mere exaggerations. However, once you have found a course that achieves even a minor result in any such investigation, it is quite amazing how mere refinement may enhance the trend, and how the methods used seem automatically to suggest more efficient variations in related fields that carry the whole enterprise forward to unexpected conclusions. To use the parable form of exposition: consider the invention of gunpowder as an explosive force— allegedly by the Chinese a very long time ago—and where it has ended up today in the form of H-bombs and so forth. The idea of animals getting their oxygen out of a liquid instead of a gas is as unique as the idea of an explosion *per se* once was.

Perhaps then, "walking for water" might be achieved by the use of drugs, but everyone with whom I have discussed this bizarre business, and notably West Africans, seem to lean to another notion. This would seem to center around what we call rather loosely, hypnosis. This category of "suggestion", however, seems more applicable to the first case where the people were apparently inert. And this brings us to a particular aspect of the class of events which the non-specialist lumps together as hypnotism.

An age-old "trick" of the fakirs is to be buried alive. There is no doubt about this any longer (as numerous fully controlled case histories attest). I have a file on a case reported by the Medical Department of a British colony which was supervised by five doctors including the Senior Medical Officer, Dr. Rex Cheverton, who is a very prominent authority today. In this case the performer was a Mexican of predominantly Amerindian blood, who, after being examined physically, was buried for twenty-four hours under two truckloads of gooey earth on the main plaza of the capital city of British Honduras, Belize, in full view of the populace, by permission of the Governor, and under police guard.

My friend, the Senior Medical Officer, tells me[44] that the man's condition was other than catalepsis in that, while an extremely faint pulse was detectable, even with a stethoscope no sign whatsoever of breathing was detectable. In other words, this was one of the stages between catalepsis (which is defined as "feigning death") and true suspended-animation. Further, whether he had truly stopped breathing for the duration or if he had reduced his rate of doing so to such an extent that even a medical man could not detect it, he could obviously survive for twenty-four hours, virtually without it. Of course there was some air in the material under which he was buried, but this material was gooey, i.e., saturated, so that almost the entire amount of any free oxygen available would be dissolved in water. Did the man do without oxygen or did he obtain enough from this source to keep his greatly slowed metabolism going? Then again, how did he do it?

That this man did do this shows that others can do it, and there is no reason why a whole village could not be taught the "art" from an early age. The Ibibio are essentially a "water people" and what could be a better form of defense from persistent slavers—and don't forget there was slaving for millenia in Africa before the wretched white men arrived.

But what of those active men cheerily gathering clams in salt water? There was manifestly no catalepsis involved here—unless, of course. . . .

It was an African and a West African who has given

me the only hint as to the workings of this business by stating in a most matter of fact way that among the "bush men" (as he rather scathingly called all tribalized citizens of his country who have not yet been contaminated by western ways) there were known ways of stemming the flow of blood, regulating the circulation, and (what intrigued me most) controlling the retention and *reabsorption* of urine in case of need during the temporary absence of anything to drink. (Be it noted that the bladder is just as much a storage organ as it is a mere convenience to the process of elimination. Otherwise, why do wholly aquatic frogs of some kinds retain such large bladders?)

I have witnessed the stemming of blood-flow many times, and even by a highly aristocratic and wealthy school-friend of mine of French-Mexican ancestry. He once carved my wife's initials on his arm in a restaurant. It made an awful mess until he said he would stop it. And this he did instantly for, when he wiped his arm with a table napkin, there were the livid, deep, and open cuts (several inches *in toto*) but not a drop of blood, while before it had been flowing like an artesian well. He even pulled the sleeve of his tuxedo down and got up and danced. At the end of the evening we asked to see the cuts. They had mostly closed and were perfectly dry and bloodless. (This chap also used to chew-up champagne glasses *and* swallow them, and he once stopped a chattering dowager dead in the middle of a sentence by sticking a steak knife right through both his cheeks and then biting down on the blade! He was quite a pixie.)

Overall catalepsis I can go for, and the control of selected bodily functions seems possible, but I just don't see where the Senegalese fisher-folk got the "fuel" to run on while engaged in anything so strenuous as underwater clamming. Trouble is, I can't find anybody in our world who will even discuss the matter sensibly and from a scientific point of view. On the other hand, I can't find any West Africans—black, white, brown, yellow, or striped— who have any further information on, or reports of, the whole business. One would have thought that this would be a golden opportunity for liars and other story-tellers. Perhaps it is too big a lie; perhaps they just don't have the imagination; perhaps, however, it's the truth. If it is, I strongly suggest that it be investigated at the earliest possible moment, though I don't suppose the manufacturers of skin-diving equipment would be too happy. I might say "Have Faith" but that is beyond the pale of science.

Part III

MORE NASTY THINGS

Chapter 8.

FROZEN MAMMOTHS[45]

A CARTOON APPEARED in the *Saturday Evening Post* some years ago showing two scientists staring at a small pile of dust in the middle of a laboratory bench. This was captioned, "Of course, nobody really wanted a dehydrated elephant, but it's nice to see what we can do."

Nobody, as far as I have been able to ascertain, wants to quick-freeze an elephant, but the idea has begun to interest some people in the frozen-foods industry since I started asking if they could tell me how to do such a thing. The reason for my question is simply that we already have lots of frozen elephantines; the flesh of some of them has retained its full flavor, and I wanted to know how the job was done. There is one corpse in particular that is exceptionally irksome. This is the famous Beresovka mammoth that was thawed out of the frozen earth or "muck" of northern Siberia just after the turn of this century.

About one-seventh of the entire land surface of our earth, stretching in a great swath round the Arctic Ocean, is permanently frozen. The surface of some of this territory is bare rock, but the greater part of it is covered with a layer, varying in thickness from a few feet to more than 1000 feet, of stuff we call "muck". This is composed of an assortment of different substances, all bound together with frozen water, which becomes and acts like rock. While its actual composition varies considerably from place to place, it is usually composed of fine sand or coarse silt, but it also includes a high proportion of earth or loam, and often masses of bones or even whole animals in various stages of preservation or decomposition. There is so much of the latter on occasion that even strong men find it almost impossible to stand the stench when it is melting. This muck is spread all across northern Asia and is exceptionally widespread in Northern Siberia. It appears again in Alaska, and lies right across the top of Canada almost to Hudson Bay.

The list of animals that have been thawed out of this

mess would cover several pages. It includes the famous woolly mammoths and woolly rhinoceroses, horses like those still existing wild in Asia, giant oxen and huge kinds of cats and dogs. In Alaska it also includes giant bison, wolves, and beavers, and an apparently quite ordinary lion as well as many other animals now extinct and some which are still in existence, like the musk-ox and the ground squirrel. The presence of the extinct species provides us with a fine set of riddles, and of those that are not extinct, with another set; and the absence of still others (like man) provide us with a third set. The greatest riddle, however, is when, why, and how did all these assorted creatures, and in such absolutely countless numbers, get killed, mashed up, and frozen into this horrific indecency?

There was a time when there hardly seemed to be any real mystery here, apart from the preservation of animals long since extinct—in what was sometimes a perfect state. When western science first became aware of the matter, they summarily dismissed it with the classic statement that "the animals fell into the ice". And, for quite a time, this suggestion seems to have proved quite satisfactory to most people; those who murmured that one cannot fall into *ice* were hushed by dismal accounts of Swiss mountaineers falling into crevasses in glaciers.

It came to light, however, that there are not—and never were—any glaciers in Siberia except on the upper slopes of a few mountains, and that the animals are never found on mountains, but always on the level plains only a little above sea level. Further, it was pointed out that no bit of one has ever been found *in* ice. They are all in the muck.

These facts indicated water as the agency which engulfed the creatures. It was explained that they fell into rivers and were then deposited miles away in deltas and estuaries under layers of silt. This sounded splendid at first, but then the next group of riddles appeared. These animal remains were not in deltas, swamps, or estuaries, but were scattered all over the country. Almost without exception, they were stuck in the highest levels of the curious, flat, low plateaus that occur all over the tundra between the river valleys. It was also pointed out that the whole of Northern Asia, Alaska, and Western Canada could never have been one vast delta, nor could their rivers have wandered about all over this higher land, depositing muck *uphill*. But last, and worst of all, a number of these animals were perfectly fresh, whole and undamaged, and still either standing or at least kneeling upright.

A mammoth falling into a river filled with melt-water is not going to be carried along in an upright position and deposited thus miles away. Also, elephants are very good swimmers in any case, and, owing to the huge amounts of vegetable matter they must keep in their stomachs at all times and which develop much gas, it is well-nigh impossible to sink them. Before this can be accomplished they have to be in an advanced state of decomposition or even to have burst. Then their remains would be shoved, bumped and probably rolled over and over along the bottom of the river before coming to rest in their final silty graves. But these standing animals were perfect, not burst, and with their fur coats in good order; they were not decomposed. On the contrary, their flesh was perfectly preserved. So the water theory had to be abandoned.

Next, mud became popular. There are certain kinds of clays found on the tundra only a few inches of which are sticky enough to hold a man by his feet; and so some intrepid Russian scientists suggested that, given a few feet of this substance, it could hold a mammoth till he froze to death. Despite the fact that no such substance has ever been found either holding or lying under any frozen animal, this idea at first came almost as a relief and was heartily adopted by almost everybody. But there are always, it seems, some spoil-sports in mammoth hunting; they pointed out not only the above fact but also that this hypothetical "goo" would have had to be unfrozen at the time, and that this could only mean that the temperature of the air was well above freezing. The animals must therefore have been frozen *after* death—probably by starvation—in which case they would have fallen over and started to decompose. Two emendations were therefore proposed.

The first was the idea that the animals fell into gulches, breaking down the banks as they fell and being engulfed in mud, and then that a sudden drop in temperature took place and they were frozen, upright. The other was that, after they got stuck, a gigantic blizzard blew up and froze both them and the goo forever. Both theories sounded possible, but both were immediately shown to be impossible. It was particularly this Beresovka specimen that proved this.

The Beresovka mammoth was discovered by a Siberian tribesman around the turn of the century.[46] It was sticking headfirst out of a bank of the Beresovka River, a tributary of the mighty Kolyma which empties into the Arctic Ocean. This man axed off the tusks and took them to sell at the nearest trading post, at Yakutsk, and there he told the Cossack who bought them about the rest of the animal. Now there was an ukase promulgated by the Czar in force at that time, stating that all mammoth or other frozen-animal discoveries were to be reported to the government. This the Cossack did, and a scientific expedition was sent by the National Academy of Sciences from St. Petersburg. The members of this company built a shack over the corpse and lighted fires within to thaw it out. They then dismembered it carefully, packed up the parts, refroze them in the air outside and sledded them to the Trans-Siberian Railroad.[47]

This corpse was sort of squatting at the back-end, but was raised on one foreleg in front, with the other held forward as if about to salute. Much of the head, which was sticking out of the bank, had been eaten down to the bone by local wolves and other animals, but of the rest most was perfect. Most important, however, was that the lips, the lining of the mouth, and the tongue were preserved. Upon the last, as well as between the teeth, were portions of the animal's last meal, which for some almost incomprehensible reason it had not had time to swallow.

This meal proved to have been composed of delicate sedges and grasses and—most amazing of all—fresh buttercup flowers. The stomach contained many more quarts of similar material. This discovery, in one fell swoop, just about demolished all the previous theories about the origin of these frozen animals and negated almost everything that was subsequently put forward. In fact, it presented a royal flush of new riddles.

First, the mammoth was upright, but it had a broken hip. Second, its exterior was whole and perfect, with none of its two-foot-long shaggy fur rubbed or torn off. Third, it was fresh; its parts, although they started to rot when the heat of the fire got at them, were just as they had been in life; the stomach contents had not begun to decompose. Finally, there were these buttercups on its tongue.

Perhaps none of these things sound very startling at first, but if you will examine them, one at a time, employing simple logic and good, common horse-sense, you will immediately find that they add up to an incredible picture. Let us take the points in succession.

That the animal had a broken hip shows that some very strong force must have been exerted upon it either before or after death. By the position of the corpse it would at first seem that this was caused before death by the animal's falling into one of the famous gulches and then having struggled to get out with its forefeet. However, there is no reason why the fracture could not have taken place after the animal was dead and be due to some great weight placed upon it while loose material remained beneath it. The animal may, indeed, have slipped and injured itself, though from what or into what there is absolutely no evidence. It had obviously not been either inundated or washed away by a flood, and it had not been drowned. Third, and very importantly, it was not only frozen but perfectly so, and here is where we come to the first of the more vital points.

Freezing meat is not quite so simple a process as one might think. It will jell once you drop the temperature below freezing, and theoretically it will remain forever, provided its contained moisture does not melt. So also will a whole corpse. However, the frozen-food technicians have discovered two vital facts. The first is that simply freezing meat is not sufficient, because it loses its flavor and finally becomes unfit for human consumption after a time if it is only just *frozen*. To preserve it properly, temperatures of minus-twenty degrees Fahrenheit or lower are needed. The second and more important point is that to preserve it at all it must be frozen very rapidly, and the faster the better. The slower the job is done, the larger are the crystals that form in the water and other liquids contained in its cells; the faster the process, the smaller they are. Above a certain size, these crystals burst the cells. The meat then becomes dehydrated on being unfrozen, and loses all its flavor.

The flesh of many of the animals found in the muck must have been very rapidly and deeply frozen, for its cells were not burst and, although one mammoth has been found by the radiocarbon dating method to be just over 10,000 years old, the flesh of these animals was remarkably fresh and some was devoured by the explorers' sledge dogs.

At *minus 40° Fahrenheit*, it takes twenty minutes to quick-freeze a dead turkey and thirty to preserve a whole side of beef. But these are mere bits of meat, not live animals clothed in fur and containing blood, internal organs and food, at a living temperature of about 98°.

The problem is to extract all the heat from the whole beast, but this can only be done from the outside—and by working inward. Unless we have tremendous cold outside, the center of the animal—and notably its stomach—will remain comparatively warm for some time, probably long enough for decomposition to start in its contents, while the actual chilling of the flesh will be slow enough for large crystals to form within its cells. Neither event occurred with the mammoths.

Here we must digress for a moment to consider a related riddle—namely, how these animals were all killed so suddenly. (And please note, I do not mean at the same time.) Temperatures of lower than minus-100° Fahrenheit have recently been recorded in Antarctica, and the air customarily registers much less than zero over wide areas of the earth, yet very large numbers of animals live happily at such temperatures. Sled-dogs burrow into the snow to sleep in Antarctica and thereby obtain some protection, but they also stand about in the open for hours, even when a near hurricane is blowing—and moving air has a much greater chilling effect than still air. Men, though admittedly well clothed, have been out in temperatures of minus-100° for up to half an hour—and in a roaring blizzard to boot—without their lungs freezing; but much more amazing were the little Shetland ponies that Scott took on his ill-fated dash to the South Pole in 1911. He got these to the dome of the Antarctic icecap, and they had to stand out in the open all the time, yet they survived as long as their food supply lasted. In fact, it takes a very great deal of cold to kill a warm-blooded animal, and especially one that is already somewhat inured to it.

It now transpires, from several studies, that mammoths, though covered in a thick underwool and a long overcoat— and in some cases having quite a layer of fat—were not specially designed for arctic conditions; a little further consideration will make it plain that they did not live in such conditions.

That they did not live perpetually or even all year round on the arctic tundra is really very obvious. First, the average Indian elephant, which is a close relative of the mammoth and just about the same size, has to have several hundred pounds of food daily just to survive. For more than six months of the year, there is nothing for any such creature to eat on the tundra, and yet there were tens of thousands of mammoths. Further, not one trace of pine needles or of the leaves of any other trees were in the stomach of the Beresovka mammoth; little flowering buttercups, tender sedges and grasses were found exclusively. Buttercups will not grow even at forty degrees, and they cannot flower in the absence of sunlight. A detailed analysis of the contents of the Beresovka mammoth's stomach brought to light a long list of plants, some of which still grow in the arctic, but are actually much more typical of *southern* Siberia today. Therefore, the mammoths either made annual migrations north for the short summer, or the part of the earth where their corpses are found today was somewhere else in warmer latitudes at the time of their death, or both.

Here is a really shocking (to our previous way of thinking) picture: Vast herds of enormous, well-fed beasts not specifically designed for extreme cold, placidly feeding in sunny pastures, delicately plucking flowering buttercups, at a temperature in which we would probably not even have needed an overcoat. Suddenly they were killed and sometimes without any visible sign of violence and before they could so much as swallow a last mouthful of food, and then were quick-frozen so rapidly that every cell of their bodies is perfectly preserved, despite their great bulk and their high temperature. What, we may well ask, could possibly do this?

Fossils of plants requiring sunlight every day of the year—which is far from the condition pertaining about the poles—have been found in Greenland and on Antarctica. This alone proves that at some time in the past either the poles have not been where they are now, or those portions of the earth's surface that lie about the poles today were once elsewhere. Astronomers and engineers concur in stating that the rotational axis of the earth cannot ever have shifted because the earth is a vast flywheel, and even if any force great enough could be found to so shift it, it would fly apart.

Ergo, the crust of the earth must have shifted. Whether it did so in bits and the bits then shifted around reciprocally as suggested by Wegener, or whether it moved as a whole as propounded by Hapgood[48] cannot be debated here. The latter seems the more probable at present, but in either case, if the crust does from time to time come unstuck from the central body of the spinning earth, it will start to move and new parts of it will drift in under the poles. However, the circumference at the equator bulges by twenty-six miles compared with the mean average circumference of the earth as measured north and south through the poles. This means that any portion of the crust heading for the equator is going to have to stretch by thirteen miles, while any moving toward a pole will have to contract by the same amount. And what must then happen?

The crust of the earth is estimated to be variously between twenty and sixty miles thick. This is really very little compared to the whole earth, being only about as thick as the outer skin of an onion. Its rocks are to some extent plastic, but are like taffy in that they can be stretched slowly, but will break if pulled too fast. Therefore, if a part of the crust goes up over the rise of the equator too fast, it will crack open and form vast rockbergs, while the material from the layer beneath it will come welling up to fill these cracks and sometimes even to flow out in great sheets such as are found all over the earth. Also, both about the equator and toward the poles, where the crust is being squeezed, every available volcano will be set off.

Now, volcanoes, when in eruption, not only spew out lava and hurl out rocks but also eject masses of dust particles, steam and other gases. Some of the dust may be shot into the upper atmosphere and then drift all around the earth. After the Indonesian island of Krakatoa blew up in 1883, there were magnificent sunsets all over the earth for several years because of this dust. Other great volcanic eruptions have actually affected rainfall because moisture gathers around small particles, and the gases—notably carbon dioxide, if present—have a marked effect upon the content of the atmosphere. It has been estimated that if only twenty major volcanoes went off at the same time, all manner of positively terrifying things could happen to our old earth and thus also to both us and mammoths. In fact, this may be the answer to most of our riddles. This theory is buttressed by the fact that great layers of volcanic dust have been found interlarded with the muck in Alaska.

A sudden mass extrusion of dust and gases would cause the formation of monstrous amounts of rain and snow, and it might even be so heavy as to cut out sunlight altogether for days, weeks, or months if the crustal movements continued. Winds beyond anything known today would be whipped up, and cold fronts of vast lengths would build up with violent extremes of temperature on either side. There would be forty days and nights of snow in one place, continent-wide floods in another, and roaring hurricanes, seaquakes, and earthquakes bringing on landslides and tsunamis (so-called tidal waves) in others, and many other disturbances. But perhaps most important may have been the gases which would probably have been shot up highest of all. What would happen to them?

And this is where we get back to quick-freezing mammoths, for the frozen-food experts have pointed out that to do this, starting with a healthy, live specimen, you would have to drop the temperature of the air surrounding it down to a point well below minus-150° Fahrenheit.[49] There are two ways of freezing rapidly—one is by the blast method, the other by the mist process; these terms explain themselves. Moreover, the colder air or any other gas becomes, the heavier it gets. If these volcanic gases went up far enough they would be violently chilled and then, as they spiralled toward the poles, as all the atmosphere in time does, they would begin to descend. When they came upon a warm layer of air, they would weigh down upon it and pull all the heat out of it and then would eventually fall through it, probably with increasing momentum and perhaps in great blobs, pouring down through the weakest spot. And if they did this, the blob would displace the air already there, outward in all directions and with the utmost violence. Such descending gases might well be cold enough to kill and then instantly freeze a mammoth.

Consider now our poor mammoth placidly munching away in his meadow, perhaps even under a warm sun. The sky need not even cloud over, and there need not even be a dust haze where he is living, which would appear to have then been about where Central Asia is today. All of a sudden, in a matter of minutes, the air begins to move in that peculiar way one may experience at the end of the arctic summer when the first cold front descends and the temperature may drop 60° in an hour.

All the mammoth feels is a sudden violent tingling all over his skin and a searing pain in his lungs; the air seems suddenly to have turned to fire. He takes a few breaths and expires, his lungs, throat, eyeballs, ears and outer skin already crystallized. If he is near the center of the blob, the terrible cold envelops him, and in a few hours he is a standing monument of what is virtually "rock". Nor need there be any violence until the snow comes softly to pile up on him and bury him. And here we leave him for a moment and turn to his distant cousin chewing away in Alaska, just outside the area where the blob descends. What happens to him?

The sky here probably does cloud over, and it may even start to snow, something he has not before encountered in September, when he is in the north on his summer migration. He starts to pad off for cover. But then comes a wind that rapidly grows and grows in fury and explodes into something unimaginable. He is lifted off his feet and, along with bison, lion, beaver from ponds, and fish from rivers, is hurled against trees and rocks, torn literally to bits and then bowled along to be finally flung into a seething caldron of water, mud, shattered trees, boulders, mangled grass and shrubbery and bits of his fellows and other animals. Then comes the cold that freezes the whole lot, and finally when the holocaust is over, the snow to cover it all.[50]

This is exactly the state of affairs that we find in Alaska, where the mammoths and other animals, with one or two significant exceptions, were all literally torn to pieces while still fresh.[51] Young and old alike were cast about, mangled and then frozen. There are also, however, other areas where the animals are mangled, but had time to decompose before being frozen; and still others where they decomposed down to bones and were then either frozen or not. Beyond these again, there are similar vast masses of animals, including whole herds or families, all piled together into gulleys and riverbeds and other holes, where only bones remain.

Here may be the answer to our riddle of why we find

mammoths with buttercups in their teeth in one place, shredded but still-edible mammoths in another, rotting mammoths in a third, and mammoth boneyards somewhere else. The animals were frozen whole where the blobs of cold air descended before the winds began, shredded and frozen where the winds came before the cold had spread out, and reduced to bones where the animals had time to decompose before the cold reached them or where it failed to reach.

The remains, if still sticking out of the ground where the middle of the blob occurred, would have been safely sealed in if snow came, as the Beresovka mammoth probably was. A true icecap never formed in Siberia, but there is evidence that one once started to grow there; it soon died away, and as it did so, vast floods of melt-water brought great quantities of silt *down* from the south—which is the direction the rivers flow in Siberia—and deposited it upon the compacted snow. This froze in the fall, but melted in the spring, and since a dark material absorbs more heat, it gradually, year by year, dissolved the snow below and descended upon and eventually enveloped the quick-frozen mammoth by the slow substitution of chilled silt for compacted snow.

This does not of course purport to be *the* explanation of this singular phenomenon, nor is it put forward as more than just one possible way in which what is observed could have come about. There are aspects of it that don't quite jell—and perhaps this is for once an excusable pun. Principal among these is the extremely knotty question (an inexcusable one) of just how a frozen mammoth or anything else above ground actually got into a stratum of frozen muck which is rock-hard. This is the conundrum that annoys everybody and the one over which the "experts" invariably stumble. And stumble they have, ending with a veritable outburst by a leading buffoon in a frightfully august scientific publication a few years ago (whose name shall remain off the record as I do not wish to subject anybody to outright ridicule). Trouble is, nobody has yet thought up even a possible explanation for this business apart from the one quoted above, and this, as I say, is more than just dubious. Let us examine the matter, disregarding the *causes* of whatever did happen.

In order to freeze, or rather deep-freeze, a large elephantine you have not only to *freeze* it (externally) but literally *deep*-freeze it right to its middle, and bloody fast to boot; otherwise, first the contents of its alimentary tract, and then all its internal organs, will start literally to "cook" due to the release of heat from bacterial action as in a vegetable compost heap. Now, there are those who state that this is just the way in which the insides of these mammoths *did* get themselves preserved, and I will second the motion in that I once spent three weeks on a tropical beach cutting up a fifty-foot sperm whale that had manifestly been dead for months, and found that the muscular tissue deep inside was perfectly "fresh" and neither "blue" (as we say of completely raw steaks) nor overdone. So far so good, at least for the inside; but what of the outside?

If there was a drop of some 150° to 200° in the air temperature, the integument and any bits and pieces sticking out, like eyeballs and genitalia, would indeed by almost instantly deep-frozen. However, the (non-deep-freeze) experts should be informed that such an outer coating of deep-freeze is the best way to insulate the next layers within a solid, sealed body. Don't forget that "cold" is not the opposite of "heat"; it is the natural state, while heat is but a molecular agitation. Thus, you cannot draw cold out of anything, but you can dissipate heat. By this score, "cold" cannot diffuse into a body; rather, said body has to disseminate or diffuse its heat, thereby becoming what we call "colder"; and in the case of a thing like a mammoth this will take quite some time when it is enshrined in an insulating capsule of deep-freeze. So there are problems in the middle layers too.

But next, the really vital question. Whether you get the damned thing deep-frozen all through or not, how do you get it into a solid mass of something else deep-frozen, without destroying or damaging its outside and/or without said outside rotting due to warming-up, and refreezing? This is where the theory that the Beresovska mammoth got hit and instantly killed and frozen on the surface—i.e., in air—and was subsequently "buried" breaks down. That it was so, however, is obvious and, what is more, it is almost as sure that it was frozen first and then buried later, rather than the other way around—*vide* the perfect condition of its exterior *and* (don't forget) the little buttercups. The idea that it was first covered with snow and that this then compacted to firn, and thence to ice (glacial type), and finally to palaeocrystic or "fossil" ice is perfectly splendid; but how then did the *muck* get in the act? There are only two alternatives: either there never was any snow or ice in the first and second places but an overwhelming tide of muck came along immediately after the elephantine deep-freezing event; or said snow and ice was gradually *replaced* by muck. But neither of these ideas work either.

First, the thing could not have been overwhelmed by muck because said muck would have also been deep-frozen and therefore of the consistency of a rock. (That it would have had to flow uphill is something else, and a point the advocators of this theory will have to explain.) Second, again how did successive floods of muck, warm enough to be plastic, flow uphill and, more so how could the outside of the frozen beast—standing presumably now in pristine isolation like a statue due to the warmed temperature which presumably melted all snow and ice—fail to melt and so rot; and when a hairy beast rots from the outside in a moist atmosphere, the first thing that happens is that the outer layer of the skin sloughs off. No, dear experts, these ideas just won't work. You can't have it both ways and you seemingly can't have it either way this time; yet there are the bloody animals to prove that you *must* have it.

I suppose you will say at this point: "OK, you think you're so damned smart, *you* tell us what happened." Well, I can't, and after some thirty years on this bit I don't think I am going to try any more. There are those that seem to feel I am advocating some kind of cataclysm to account for all these mass deaths, and cataclysms unnerve everybody, let alone scientists. I am not advocating such, though I do think that the suddenly descending globs of super-cold air would seem to go further than any other theory to explain the results observable. As to the procedure and process for freezing the stuff I can but rely on the real experts in the meat industry. When it comes to floods of non-frozen muck running uphill I tend to give up, since I know, as a trained geologist, that the very idea is totally illogical though I suppose nothing is impossible. But getting a solid, deep-frozen elephantine into a solid mass of rock completely buffaloes (or should I say "elephants") me. If only somebody who knows what he or she is talking about would come up with a suggestion that might at least work on logical grounds or in accord with our present knowledge of physics, I would not only be happy but I could start making preparations for my wake. So, I am the executive secretary of a society stated to be founded for "The Investigation of the Unexplained". Splendid; but so help me!

Chapter 9.

VILE VORTICES[52]

WHEN THE U.S. NUCLEAR SUBMARINE, the *Scorpion*, turned up missing in July, 1968, there was an outburst of emotion, speculation, and a peculiar frenzy that was not confined to the United States. It was a terrible tragedy from the human point of view, but, horrible as it may sound, there was nothing really unique about it. Ships have been going down since the dawn of maritime history. So have planes, and now space vehicles and submarines. So what was so exceptional about the disappearance of the *Scorpion*?

First, it was a nuclear-powered sub; but second, it *could* have gone down in a sea country that is alleged to be of a very special and peculiar nature. [Actually, it didn't; it was found 400 miles south of the Azores.]

Many subs have just plain vanished, and not only in wartime. Two of them disappeared at the same time in the Mediterranean only a short time before—one Israeli, the other French. Also, we have lost other nuclear-powered subs, such as the *Thresher*. Whenever a sub fails to surface, there is an emotional outburst. And why not, since almost all of us are basically claustrophobics. But sometimes there enters another ingredient in these sorry events—namely, mystery.

Just how to define this has not as yet been determined or even attempted. Why is it that the public singles out one horror from all the countless others that occur every day and concentrates on it to the exclusion of all else? As I say, submarines have been staying down since they were invented and there have been some very dramatic rescue stories; but when two go down in the same sea, as in the Mediterranean recently, the story often just sort of dies away. The individual event, in fact, seems to be of less importance than the *place* where it occurs. Ships have been going down in the Mediterranean since long before Greek times. By the same token, all three classes of craft have been ditching in the North Atlantic one way or another for centuries. In fact, they have been going down all over the world, but only the maritime historians pay much attention. Yet, if so much as one dirty old freighter disappears in certain areas, thousands of people start speculating. In the case of the *Scorpion,* half the reading public of the world seems to have gone balmy. Why?

There is a sort of folklore building up about a certain area in the North Atlantic that has been tagged with a very catchy title: "The Bermuda Triangle". I am still not quite sure where this monicker originated but it was the popular writer, Vincent Gaddis, who first "put it on the map", as it were, in an article in *Argosy* in 1964.[53] The inference here is that there is a roughly triangular area with sides running from Bermuda to central Florida and thence to Puerto Rico in which a large number of complete *disappearances,* rather than mere founderings of ships, have been recorded throughout the years, and over which an exceptional number of planes have simply vanished without a trace.

This is a glamorous notion, but I am afraid that, on proper analysis, it does not stand up. It is *not* a triangle, and its periphery is much greater than the one outlined above. In fact, the area in which such disappearances, or alleged disappearances, have been recorded forms a large, sort of lozenge-shaped area which is neither centered on the oceanic island of Bermuda nor can in any other way be depended from it. We have plotted all the "disappearances"—and please note that this is something quite different from mere sinkings of ships and submarines, or ditchings of planes—reported from this area and have found that it slops way over the original so-called "triangle".

After this discovery, the question naturally arose as to the uniqueness of this funny blob, which extends from about 30° to 40° north latitude, and from about 55° to 85° west. Was it unique?

We knew already that there was at least one other such area alleged to exist.[54] This lies some 250 miles south of the Japanese island of Honshu about longitude 140° east.

We therefore started to work, gathering records of ships lost and planes vanishing around this point which, as a matter of fact, had up until then been only mentioned—and rather casually, at that. The outcome was not just amazing; it was positively startling. Plane after plane on its way south to Guam appears to have vanished; so we started plotting again, and despite the usually very vague locations given—and no wonder, considering these ships and planes disappeared without radio signals or any trace—another lozenge-shaped blob came to light.

This startled us a bit, but then one of my colleagues had the brilliant idea of getting out a map of the world! Once we had a map before us, we saw that both lozenges lay roughly about 30° north and also spread about 30° east to west latitudinally. This really did spark us, so we made a concerted grab for a globe.

Now the surface of our earth as seen on a globe is really very different from what we look at on a two-dimensional map, and especially one made on what is called the Mercator Projection. Just where did these two blobs lie relative to each other as one went around the globe? It turned out that they were 160° apart (going around one way) and 200° (going the other). In other words, there did not appear to be any noticeable pattern. If they had been at 180° going both ways, they would have been exactly opposite each other on opposite sides of the earth. But then something else cropped up.

We had been inundated with letters asking for more information on the *disappearances* of the Israeli and French submarines at east and west ends of the Mediterranean respectively. We were naturally unable to add anything to the news reports and official statements. However, I think we do now have something to offer. The Mediterranean Sea happens to form a lozenge-shaped blob, also lying between thirty and forty degrees north, and just about thirty degrees from left to right latitudinally.

Naturally, we measured the distances between these three blobs Then something else rather startling came to light. They were arranged on an apparently strict numerical progression—between Bermuda to the Mediterranean, four; the Mediterranean to the Japanese, five; and the Japanese to the Bermudan, six.

Now, I don't like such neat patterns emerging in anything in nature; it looks far too much as though we got the idea first and then tried to fit the facts into it. You can fit almost anything into anything if you try hard enough, as any mathematician, statistician, or police officer can tell you. However, Nature is to a great extent *fairly* orderly and *does* display rather neat patterns.

So we had three in a line—and the same line, please note—of something. But just what?

What set these three areas apart from all others was that large concentrations of planes, ships and subs not only went down there, but that they vanished, leaving no trace. At this point, I started doing some hard thinking. If there are three such areas between 30° and 40° north latitude, could there be equivalents at 30° and 40° south latitude? A subsequent investigation into plane, ship, and sub losses in the Southern Hemisphere yielded some amazing results.

There turned out to be three exactly similar areas situated below the equator. These lie off the east coasts of South America, South Africa and Australia. All proved to be precisely within 30° to 40° of latitude south, and also to be about 30° of longitude in width. But *very* strangely, they also were all tilted up to the right or east! Frankly, this does not seem to make sense, because our planet is a sphere and the Southern Hemisphere should *mirror* the Northern.

We started looking for some physical reason for this clear pattern. The first thing that emerged was that these vortices in the Southern Hemisphere were shifted precisely the same number of degrees to the east in all cases. Then one further fact came to light.

Of all the possible known physical factors that could cause this pattern—temperature, barometric pressure and, above all, geomagnetic anomalies—only one does fit, and this is a particular feature of surface ocean currents!

Five of these six areas (the Mediterranean alone being in a different category) lie on the right, or east, sides of the continents, and all *precisely* in curious areas where hot surface ocean currents stream out of the tropical latitudes toward the colder waters of the temperate, subpolar and eventually polar areas. What is more, the two principal ones in the Northern Hemisphere, in accordance with the simple behavior of waters on a spinning globe, turn clockwise, while the three in the Southern Hemisphere turn counterclockwise. There is nothing odd about this, but there is about the fact that these twirls all make their sharpest turns precisely in these five locations.

As there is a very good scientific reason for these twirls of hot ocean currents being just where they are, anything strange or mysterious that is common to them should probably be an outcome of their existence. (And do not for a moment think that the disappearance of planes, ships and subs is the *only* odd occurrence reported from these six areas, including the Mediterannean this time.) Other oddities include wild reports of poltergeist manifestations and an unusually high incidence of UFOs or flying saucers.

But even this was not by any means the end of the trail. I first appealed to, and then assembled a number of engineers, EM specialists, and geophysicists, and presented them with our problem and what we had found out by pure research, and then gave them a set of blank globes to go to work on. I started with my very old friend, Al Bielek, an EM engineer who lives in moral chastity with a sort of harem of slide-rules. I started with him because I wanted first to get the math and spherical geometry sorted out before we started the (as I then envisaged it) very arduous task of speculating upon, investigating, and ferreting out possible causes for what we already had; and it was lucky that we did so, as it turned out. All of them were also mathematicians, despite their working specialities, so that the session, which lasted a week, became interesting to say the least—to the non-mathematicians, that was.

I love to watch these men work. It's not unlike attending high mass. You really haven't the foggiest notion what they are doing and you may doubt the reasonableness of a lot of what they do, but you have faith and you have to keep it. (To push the analogy and be thoroughly facetious, I must add that we had to keep a constant supply of good Guinea-red and Graham wafers coming; and not only for the faithful, because sixty percent of the "high priests" present were of Italian origin)! Just about every world map we have—and we have a rather large collection—was dragged out, and I had to clear my desk and retreat into a corner. Compared to other scientists, it is astonishing how little argument there is among mathematicians. They talk their own language and they don't talk at all until their slide-rules tell them what to say. This makes for progress; and progress they made in this case, and with really very astonishing results.

To make a very long and fascinating story as brief as possible, suffice it to say that they found not six but *ten* globs, lozenges, vortices, or whatever you want to call them; five in the northern, and five in the southern hemispheres; and all 72° apart latitudinally. What is more, those in the southern hemisphere were all shifted to the (right) east by about 40° of longitude. Then again, each of the pairs (a northern and its associated southern opposite number) lay on a perfect sinusoidal curve common to all of them, the "bulge" of these curving to the west by some 20° in the north and to the east by the same amount in the south.

Now, the exact size and shape of these areas is not of course known, nor is their center known in any one case. We tried triangles, circles, and other conformations but we were forced back time and time again to a sort of lozenge-shaped blob. It was not till months later that an explanation for this came to light, and it did so in a completely different field but the very one that our group finally had decided was the only field left in which to seek an explanation. But more of this in a moment.

However, up till this stage of our enquiry, we had missed four of these lozenges: two in the east Pacific, and two in the Indian Ocean. There is very little confirmation of the first two except that some curious bowl-shaped depressions in the surface of the ocean have been reported from that in the northern Pacific. The discovery of the northern blob about the Persian Gulf, however, really brought us up sharp. The things that have been reported as having taken place around there for millenia are positively hair-raising, but this will just have to await separate treatment at another time. That the two in the southern hemisphere were missed is hardly surprising as practically nobody has ever, or ever does, go there, either by plane, ship, or sub.

The regularity of placement of these blobs must mean something. We had nothing to go on but my prior conclusion that the initial six that we had spotted lay in sort of "whirligigs" of hot surface water. But then the EM boys came charging in, insisting that the things must be five pairs of dipoles. When asked to demonstrate this they got into their only real argument with the mathematicians, so that I had to revert to my expertise, which I like to regard as the practical. So, getting five skewers and by sacrificing one of the globes, we were able to demonstrate that the EM boys were right; once you found the right glob in the opposite hemisphere to come out at, all five skewers were fighting to pass through the precise center of the earth! So, Lo! What do we have here?

Are these sort of vast bar-magnets that pass right through the earth, and if so how come they go *straight* through if their points of ingress and egress lie "opposite" but upon sinusoidal curves—or do they? They ought to form a sort of 'x'-sided framework around the center of the earth. It needs some knowledge of stereograms to visualize this, something I struggled to achieve for three years when studying crystallography but in which I failed completely, so I have to rely on what these wretched people said.

Anyhow, the point is there are eight known and two suspected areas on the surface of our earth, all either wholly or substantially in the hydrosphere, where planes, ships and/or subs just vanish and around which lots of other anomalies and funny things happen. If these blobs form the ends (or dipoles) of somethings that pierce the earth, what could be their cause and therefore their effects?

The tremendous popular interest in the Bermuda Triangle was started by flying-saucer buffs, apparently for two reasons. First, a lot of UFOs have been reported from the skies over this area by utterly reliable flyers, both military and commercial. Second, even the most pompous "ufologist" still has a sneaking idea that flying saucers are machines and must therefore be made by very clever chaps who live elsewhere in the universe and come here for one purpose or another. On this account, UFO buffs immediately claimed that this Bermuda Triangle was some kind of special place the "space people" had picked out to use as a sort of collecting ground.

That at least five of these areas are where hot tropical surface-waters jet in comparatively narrow streams into cold-water areas *is* of enormous significance. These are the areas of extreme temperature variabilities which alone would predicate a very high incidence of violent marine and aerial disturbances. What more likely areas for storms and wrecks and founderings, and even magnetic anomalies? Moreover, since all these areas also happen to be major areas of human population and maritime enterprise, is it a small wonder that they would be those wherein the most losses of ships, planes and subs would be recorded? However, there still remains one really mysterious factor.

Planes, ships and subs have, as we have stressed, been disappearing all over the world. But it has to be admitted that many *more* are reported to have done so in these areas than in any others; and, what is much more important, *the number of disappearances is out of all proportion to such recorded losses anywhere else.* This is the point upon which not only our Navy, but a lot of other navies, maritime commissions and even Lloyd's of London have become baffled.

When a ship or plane sinks into the sea, *something* almost invariably comes back to the surface. A large liner goes down, and it may be a month before so much as one wooden deck chair surfaces; a small plane ditches, and the whole area is immediately covered with an oil slick, then all sorts of bits and pieces surface within an hour. But these are ditchings, founderings, sinkings or just plain wrecks. Disappearances are something else. In our mysterious areas, planes, ships, and subs just *vanish;* not a trace remains. What is more, there is a quite uncanny sudden cutoff of radar and radio contact.

I would like to state that the disproportionately high number of losses in these "vile vortices" is due only to the fact that they fall in very rough areas of contrary currents, winds, temperature inversions and so forth, but I am afraid I can *not* do so. Allowing for all of these, we still have to explain this business of disappearances, *per se.* And this is where the flying-saucer boys seem to have us over a barrel.

Since we never get any facts as to just what did happen in these cases, how can we even start to try to explain them? The services, and notably the air forces and navies, know perfectly well that there is something "not right" about this, but they haven't any more idea than we have as to what it could be. Thus, the picture is wide open to suggestions—most unfortunately, and particularly, from those who have none of the known facts! As I have said above, the most vociferous are the UFO buffs who have suggested that these "vortices" are holes where *gravity,* earth magnetism and perhaps other natural features, are weaker or otherwise different from those elsewhere around the surface of our planet. They have then proceeded from this assumption to the speculation that extraterrestrial intelligencies may know of these anomalies and have picked these vortices through which to descend upon us and collect specimens of us and our machines.

While I am no longer willing to say that anything is *impossible*, I have the gravest doubts about all such theories. Admittedly, there is a very great deal that is odd about these areas, but there are enough *known* natural oddities about them (that we do not yet fully understand) to possibly account for all of the strange happenings therein.

What *do* we really know of the gravitational, electromagnetic and other effects of a gigantic whirlpool—or maelstrom—of water? What of the composition of not only the water itself, but of other elements dissolved in it? Look what's turning up in the foggy field of dowsing, for example. How do we know what gravitational anomalies may not be projected *upward* in such areas that might black-out compasses and/or cause some natural phenomenon that sort of opens up our space-time-continuum and lets planes and other things "drop out"? And, we might add, that allows all sorts of odd junk to *drop in* as well?

This chapter is, as explained in my acknowledgements up front, a rewrite of an article published in *Argosy* Magazine six months prior to the time of rewriting and before we had undertaken the more detailed researches described above. It may be of interest therefore to quote my ending to that article. This went as follows: "This, you may rightly say, is getting quite 'far out'. I agree, but will somebody please come up with an explanation or even a suggestion as to just where all these planes, ships and possibly submarines, *do* go?"

I cannot answer the last question but, literally, as of the time of writing this, a new and much more cogent suggestion as to what these things themselves may be has cropped up. This appeared in a highly technical paper by a Dr. John Carstoiu, of International Consultant Scientists Corporation, of Brookline, Mass., entitled "The Two Gravitational Fields and Gravitational Waves Propagation."[55] The research reported therein was supported in part by the Office of Naval Research (under Contract No.

N00014-66-C-0217). I wouldn't deign to even try to explain this but I can state that this work represents the first step into the investigation of a second gravitational field, and shows what some of the effects of such a field must produce. Among these are some extraordinary, and sort of unearthly, anomalies in whirlpools or vortices of revolving fluids, or liquids if you will. On page four of this paper Dr. Carstoiu makes the following statement: "The relativistic effect given by [the above] formula deserves careful consideration as it may cause resonances; the latter might explain [certain] strange happenings (see 11 in bibliographical references), but we cannot elaborate here." Reference number eleven was to the above article in *Argosy*.

Chapter 10.

ROCKETS AND RACKETS

IN JANUARY OF 1967, a neatly printed, 250-page, readers-digest-sized magazine appeared on the newsstands in New York and other larger American cities, entitled *Sputnik-Monthly Digest: 50c.*[56] In accord with standard regulations, there was announced at the bottom of the inside cover: "Application to mail at second class postage rates is pending at New York, N.Y. U.S. National newsstand distribution by Eastern News Distributors, Inc., 155 West 15th Street, New York, N.Y. 10011. A copy of this material is filed with a° Department of Justice where the required registration statement of Eastern News Distributors, Inc., 155 West 15th Street, New York, N.Y. 10011, as an agent of Mezhdunarodnaya Kniga, Moscow, G-200, U.S.S.R., under the Foreign Agent Registration Act of 1948, as amended, is available for public inspection. Registration does not indicate approval of this material by U.S. Government." There are other interesting aspects to this fine little publication which incidentally is printed in Fin-

---

° Is this a typo, or how many such departments do we have?

land, to which "Advertising materials", as the publishers so succinctly put it, should be sent, care of Ajan Mainos Oy, Kasarmikatu 40. C., Helsinki 20.

I give all of this only to show the claimed status of this publication since, despite being on the stands for nearly two years now, just about everybody continues to deride it. But we will come to that later, and after we have noted that this magazine is published by the Novosti Press Agency, and has a really most distinguished masthead, led off by a list of the Chairmen of the Council of Sponsors. These are: *Messrs.* Vladimir Komarov (Astronaut), Vladimir Kirillian (Academician), Yuri Zhukov (Observer), and Nikolai Bribachev (Writer). In addition, under the heading "Members of the Council of Sponsors, Consultants" are no less than twenty-two most distinguished names including, so help us, Axel Berg, Yuri Gagarin, Pyotr Kapitsa, Dmitry Shostakovich, and even Konstantin Simonov. These are household names. The publication, in other words has the backing and approval of authority. In the first issue was a long article by one Vyacheslav Zaitsev, entitled "Visitors from Outer Space".

I have seldom had to give such an extensive introduction to anything but I deem it worthwhile on this occasion for various reasons. First of all, allegedly serious-minded popular material is not disseminated from Russia unless it is thoroughly approved. Second, nothing comes out of that country unless it *is* approved. Third, the so-called West, and notably the U.S., is wildly paranoic about anything that does; in other words they either believe it implicitly or they deny it absolutely as being nothing but propaganda. But last and most important, is that very few seem to appreciate the Slavic sense of humour or realize that that group of people even has one. It is my contention that the Russians love to twit and kid us just to see how gullible we really are—and we are. Thus, anything like this that is not presented as a down-to-earth, pompous, erudite, scientific paper should be taken with at least a grain or two of monosodium-glucomate, if not the proverbial salt. Nonetheless, the names that appear on the masthead would not be allowed unless the thing had serious objectives. So what does this Vyacheslav Zaitsev have to say?

At this juncture I should put it on record that at the bottom of the righthand column of page 8 of the first issue there appears the categoric statement that: "Anything in this issue may be reprinted or reproduced with due acknowledgement to *Sputnik*." So reproduce we will.

His article starts off with the following categoric "report":

A report by a Chinese archaeologist startled the world when it was published in 1965, for he had out of old bits of knowledge pieced together an amazing theory of space-ships on a visit to the earth 12,000 years ago. The German magazine, *Das Vegetarische Universum*, wrote of his research: 'For a quarter of a century archaeologists exploring caves in the Bayan-Kara-Ula Mountains, on the border of China and Tibet, have been finding odd-looking stone discs covered with unreadable patterns and hieroglyphs. A total of 716 such discs have been discovered, apparently dating back several thousand years.

'Like a gramophone record, each disc has a hole in its centre from which a double groove spirals its way to the circumference. The grooves are not soundtracks, but (have) the oddest writing in China and indeed the rest of the world.'

Archaeologists and decipherers of ancient writing racked their brains for two decades trying to solve the secret of the spirals. The result of the research by the Chinese archaeologist was so shattering that the Peking Academy of Pre-History banned publication of his work. Eventually permission was obtained and his four colleagues published their collective effort under the intriguing title *Groove Writing Related to Spaceships which, as Recorded on the Discs, Existed 12,000 Years Ago*.

The caves high up in the Bayan-Kara-Ula Mountains are inhabited by the Ham and Dropa tribes—frail, stunted men averaging four feet two inches in height. So far they have defied ethnic classification. In fact, any detailed information about the tribes is extremely scarce.

When deciphered, one of the hieroglyphs presumably set down by an ancient member of the Ham tribe read 'The Dropas came down from the clouds in their gliders. Our men, women and children hid in the caves ten times before the sunrise. When at last they understood the sign language of the Dropas, they realized that the newcomers had peaceful intentions . . .'

Another Ham hieroglyph expresses regret over the loss of the tribe's own spaceships during a dangerous landing in high mountains, and the failure to build new ones.

In the opinion of Chinese archaeologists, the Bayan-Kara-Ula hieroglyphs are so mysterious that their interpretation and use for scientific research require the utmost care.

To obtain further information, the discs were scraped free of adhering rock particles and sent to Moscow for study. Scientists there made two important discoveries. The discs were found to contain a large amount of cobalt and other metals—a shaking discovery. Further investigation revealed that the discs vibrate in an unusual rhythm, as if they carried an electric charge or were part of an electric circuit. The 12,000-year-old discs remain a challenge to science.

Legends of ancient China say that small, gaunt, yellow-faced men came down from the clouds. But earthly tribesmen felt a revulsion for the visitors, whose enormous heads and extremely thin, weak bodies made them look ugly, and 'some people on fast horses' beat them.

Reality seems to confirm the legends. In some of the Bayan-Kara-Ula caves archaeologists and speleologists have found 12,000-year-old vestiges of graves and skeletons. The remains belong to human beings with huge craniums and underdeveloped skeletons. The Chinese expeditions which discovered the burial grounds reported they had found 'an extinct species of ape'. But so far as is known apes do not bury each other in graves or write hieroglyphic symbols on stone discs.

What makes the issue doubly involved is that the inner walls of the caves are covered in many places with pictures of the rising sun, the moon, and the stars, spaced by a multitude of pea-sized dots (possibly tiny pictures) which seem to be approaching the Earth in a mountain area.

We will not comment on this at the moment as it would seem to concern matters that are only slightly related to that which we have in mind at this juncture. Nonetheless, we would surely like to have some names, dates, and locations for all this, and be told just where said platters are (with photos), who examined them, how they tested them for mineralogical content, and just how they were deciphered. It's all very well to say that scientists—that mystical appellation—found that they were 12,000 years old. How? Could this be a bit of "Russkie" spoofing?

But now to rather more serious matters for which at least some pictures are offered in confirmation. The good chronicler Zaitsev continues with mention of one of our favourite subjects, i.e., "Celestial Eggs". He reiterates a number of expressions from all over the world to the effect that folklore and early writings assert that human beings, or creatures looking like them, have from time to time descended upon the earth in sort of vast transparent eggs. He further points out that for "eggs" one might read globular or spindle-shaped, plastic skitter-boats used to descend from orbiting space ships. He then proceeds to some observations on biblical tales, remarking that such things as the Star of Bethlehem, which either remained stationary or jumped about, could also have been one of those spaceships in fixed orbit. So far so good; but then he presents us with quite a long dissertation upon some frescos found in 1964 in a monastery named Dechany, in Kosovskaya Metehia in southern Yugoslavia. The monastery was built, he says, in the fourteenth Century and by 1340 was known to have been embellished by many frescos. The new discoveries showed "angels" in "spaceships like the present sputniks".

This is perfectly splendid, but then comes a somewhat sour note in that the "angels" are said not to be angels, in that they don't have halos (globular plastic space helmets?) while the true angels are on the ground looking up in horror and fear and covering their eyes and/or ears in terror. This is rather jolly since the "men" in the elongated space-eggs are said to be shown holding "flying-sticks", the one ahead looking back at the one behind. They were flying from west to east it is said, but how this was determined is not stated. Zaitsev then leads us to a depiction of Christ resurrecting. This is a splendid bit since the Saviour is ensconced in a spaceship and reaching out to help haul somebody up with his outstretched hand. This chap is said to be Adam and it is further said that, in the same picture, Eve waits patiently at the other side of the ship for her turn (a likely story I doubt, and what about chivalry)! But Zaitsev observes that the monks at Dechany said the spacial- (or spatial-) eggs represented the sun and moon, and goes on to ask "But why the Sun is depicted rising in the *west* the monks could not say". One thing one must admit if the illustrations are real is that said flying eggs have perfectly splendid exhausts of the back-end type—so succinctly called in German *Raketenfahrt*.

Zaitsev then goes on to say: "One of the *papers* on the Dechany *miracle* refers to a hypothesis saying that Christ was a *man* who came down to earth from space." The *magazine* comments that such ideas are "over-bold", and that the hypothesis, if confirmed, "would basically alter the Biblical story about Christ". The fresco, it is noted, shows objects obviously resembling sputniks which "baffled layman and specialist alike". (All italics ours.) In this, one would most heartily agree and on all counts. However, we would like to know what paper and in what "magazine". Was it a truly scientific "paper" in a scientific periodical or just an article in a magazine. Words, my good Russian friends, should, in the words of that famous bourgeois socialist Philip Snowden, convey meaning.

The rest of this funny article is devoted to a round-up and survey of the whole subject of the alleged visitation by humans, or humanoids, to this earth in prehistoric, ancient, and classical (western) times. Most of this is old-hat but the author offers a few items that we had not heard of before, notably from Slavic folklore and fairytale. This is a worthwhile survey as it brings together such a very large number of globally widespread beliefs of this nature. Adding Zaitsev's to others that he does not mention, it appears that such a belief is inherent in the myth, legend, and folklore of just about every people in the world both extinct and living. Moreover, there is a certain cohesion in the details of these beliefs based primarily on an assumption that, while manlike creatures evolved on and were indigenous to this earth, *True Man* is a more advanced breed of much older stock which evolved elsewhere and which has visited us from time to time, and has sometimes interbred with us. These super- or better-men are invariably said to have come down from the skies in some form of "celestial egg", to have introduced agriculture, writing, mathematics, knowledge of astronomy, the idea of religion with a priesthood involving "mysteries" to awe the local bumpkins forming a ruling hierarchy, and other unpleasantnesses.

Now, curiously, almost every case of such visitations has some connotation of the color *blue;* but this we will take up in a minute. Herewith suffice it to say that the underlying suggestion in all this, is that there is what we now call "parallel evolution" throughout the universe or at least our galaxy, and that humanoid types have come here from time to time for a variety of reasons. At the same time, there is a distinct implication that the ancients were groping after another concept, namely that life as a whole was *planted* on this earth either deliberately or by mistake (contamination of spaceships) in the first place and that the evolution ending in human beings was a sort of long-term breeding experiment or a deliberate nursery project which, in either case, has to be watched carefully and guided from time to time by deliberate interference, including artificial insemination of a purely physical nature.

Regardless of whether any of this hypothesizing and speculation has any validity, it is very interesting to note how ancient man by simply "taking thought upon the matter" nibbled away at theories that we today fully accept—to wit, evolution, exobiology, time-contraction and anomalies of the Einsteinian variety, religious mysteries, and things like the origin of agriculture. The sudden appearance of writing and mathematics in Sumeria has always baffled the prehistorians, while the Ancient Egyptian priests are recorded as having told the Greeks that they obtained both these arts along with a lot else from "The Oldtime People". Just who *these* were is not specified, but they were alleged to have mapped the whole earth and to have deposited actual maps along with all manner of information on geomorphology and geophysics, astronomy and astrophysics with the earthling priests whom they established to "civilize" the wild men of the times, control them, and put them to work. This is by no means an odd concept, and if you think it is nothing more than a wild pipe-dream get a copy of a book entitled *Maps of the Ancient Sea Kings* by Charles H. Hapgood.[59] In this scholarly work you will find categoric evidence that the coasts of the entire world were mapped some 20,000 years ago and, in the case of Antarctica, *before it was glaciated.* This is no "kookbook": the trigonometry in it alone was done by the U.S. Air Force Strategic Bomber Command.

Out of all of this there is one feature that arises to intrigue me. This is the matter of *"blueness"*. As the sky looks blue to us it may not be so odd to assume that things coming down out of the sky should get a bluish tinge at least. However, they don't, in that blue rain is not in the list (though red, black, brown, yellow, and even green are). Further, I have never heard of anybody alleging that a meteor was blue. Yet, so-called "Sky People" seem always to have been said to be blue, and not only with blue skins but with *blue blood,* so that one really does begin to wonder if there isn't something in that term as applied to aristocrats of all kinds. What a ridiculous thing to say about your rulers and leaders: *blue* blood indeed! Why not "real *red*-blooded men"? No, there is definitely something odd here and one should contemplate the very simple and perfectly well-known fact that copper can substitute for iron in what we call 'blood' as in quite a number of known animals. This can make the bones—as in certain West African frogs of the family *Rhachophoridae*— bright blue-green, and their skins if suddenly illuminated at night when all their daytime pigment has been retracted into their sebaceous photophores appear likewise.

A particularly pertinent item in this "blueness" is the matter of *woad*. This was a vegetable dye that my ancestors, the Picts of what is now called Scotland, wore in place of clothing up till the time the Romans pounded up to their borders from England. (Incidentally I take irrepressible delight in the fact that said Picts were the only people who ever stopped the Romans dead in their tracks and so bothered them that they had to build a vast wall just to try and keep them out. This sort of Maginot Line was ultimately a failure.) You may well ask "why woad" and "why blue" when the inhabitants of Scotland and Pictland employed innumerable vegetable dyes ranging all over the spectrum in color, *except for blue?* (see bibliography under *The New Yorker*).[58] Tradition has it that they so dyed themselves in imitation of, and in deference to, the "Sky People" to whom they owed allegiance, and they further claimed, as recorded by Scots and other latterday interlopers, that the Picts slipped-up somewhere or got a little too pretentious, whereupon said sky people sent a spaceship sailing down the west Atlantic coast-fringe, blasting all their hill forts, from the Lofoten Islands off northern Norway to the Canary Islands off northwest Africa. And sure enough, there are the remains of such forts all the way down this coast, most of which appear to have been hit by some intensely hot beam of something from an angle of about 45° above the offcoast Atlantic Ocean! These so-called "Fused Forts" are no joke; I've seen several myself and the piled boulders of their circular walls are turned to glass like frozen treacle on the outer-sides of the part of the wall facing the west, and the inner-side of the wall on the other side. Almost exactly the same thing has been reported by stuffy ethnologists from the western Pacific.[59]

It looks indeed as if this sort of tradition of M.L.&F. (myth, legend, and folklore, as we call it) was rife in Roman times and persisted well into the Dark and Middle Ages—as depicted in the monastery of Duchany in Yugoslavia. In fact, the idea of space people was popular for centuries before Roman times as exemplified by the worldwide cases cited by Zaitsev and others, and as seen in the extraordinarily precise descriptions in the Bible, such as Ezekiel and his bloody "Wheel" (for which be sure to consult the listing under Orton in the bibliography).[60] Since the Renaissance, and more so, since the rise of scientific methodology and the decline of religion and all other mere beliefs, this whole concept has gone underground; or, at least, it did until the modern American so-called "flying-saucer" scare got started. It is interesting therefore to do a bit of digging into the past on this score and observe just what the ancients did have to say on this matter; and here we have an absolute "lulu" to contemplate, of recent date, and absolutely matter of fact and concrete—in both senses of that word.

This one began in 1961 when archaeologists digging into Rome's famed Palatine Hill broke into a room said to have been built for, and used by, Caesar Augustus, the grandnephew of Julius Caesar. Around this room there were a number of niches with sort of false, miniature escutcheons like porticos or gateways with recessed, smooth walls at the back. (These were made of concrete!) On these walls were painted a large number of very clean and precise pictures in yellow-ochre of various shades and tones. One of these paintings thoroughly startled not only the archaeologists but everybody else. This one showed a thing like one of our more modern and faster rockets standing on four tailfins on its pad, supported by a ground-anchored taut cable and by two other slack cables from its apex. Worse still, behind it a structure was depicted in the most precise, modern, and, from an artist's point of view, dimensionally correct way, duly shaded for the same sunlight that illuminated the erect rocketlike thing. The press—i.e., the AP—said in a caption under a photograph, "Mystery is compounded by structure in background which bears striking resemblance to United Nations General Assembly Building as seen looking northeast from First Avenue (New York)".[61] And by george, it does: though we would point out that it looks a lot more like a blast-protection wall built around the periphery of some experimental rocket-launching site.

Intrigued by this extraordinary apparition, and I can call it none other, we wrote to the archaeologist in charge of the excavation which brought it to light. We received a most courteous reply that was as follows, in toto:[62]

Famous* colleague,

The picture which was reproduced in the *New York World* was actually re-discovered in a room in the basement of the house attributed to Augustus on the Palatine Hill. The story of the excavation, with reproductions of these paintings will probably be published in the near future in the Art Bulletin of the Ministry of Public Education, edited by Dr. Gianfranco Carettoni who directed the excavation; he will try to explain the mysterious object, which definitely is not a missile, but a sacred object, a stone object having divine powers, in the Alexandrian character, some refer it to the myth of Diana and Actaeon, because against the trunk is leaning a lance and a quiver, symbols of Diana. Others believe it is in the pointed shape of the club of Hercules, because there exists a similar one in the house of Livia (which is the main part of the same house of Augustus in c. d. dining room, to the right) that is in the form of a

---

*Wow!

---

great tree trunk, and supports a circle on which hangs hunting trophies (see Alinari photograph); we recognize a third example in the Museum of Naples, which came from Pompei. And here, therefore, there are many which are common and belong to a group of Alexandrian mysteries which are too much for us ... mysteries.

Cordially yours,
/Signed/G. Lugli

Now, while we thoroughly approve of this clear statement, and wish to express our sincere appreciation for its reception, we just do not accept one single word of it—at face value that is. There is, however, buried in it something more than just interesting, so let us reread Dr. Lugli's letter. We will start with the statement as to the intent of Dr. Gianfranco Carettoni, and then number the items. Thus:-

(1)"He (Dr. Carettoni) *will try to explain the mysterious object*." This is a rather sad announcement considering what comes later; and why does the poor professor have to "try" to explain it. Either it is a well-known, fully accepted, and explained item or it is not. I don't like scientists, and especially archaeologists, *trying* to explain anything. Either they should explain it or shut up.

2) *"Which definitely is not a missile"*. So help us, who said so and on what grounds? The thing looks like a missile and the great expert is going to try to explain it, so on what grounds is it definitely *not* a missile? This is pure and unadulterated bunk.

3) *"But* (it is) *a sacred object"*. Well now, how does the gallant doctor know this, and again who said so, and on what grounds. It could just as well be some bawdy phallic symbol—which, incidentally, it probably was, one way or another. My signet-ring is a sacred object; so is my wife, and every goddam tree that grows on my land.

(4) "(It is) *a stone object having divine powers"*. Here the doctor begins to lose me. On what grounds is it a representation of a *stone* object? Or does he mean that the thing is painted on stone? And, stone or not, who said it had divine powers and on what grounds? If the other professor is still getting set to try to explain it—which incidentally, he has not yet done—how can some third

party state flatly that it, or what it represents, has (had) divine powers?

(5) But: *"In the Alexandrian character"*. [We will leave this for a moment.]

(6) *"Some refer it to the myth of Diana and Actaeon"*. Who are these "some"? I have tried to find out but without success. I don't know how poor Actaeon got into this act because he was a Greek from Acte, a grandson of Cadmus, who was changed into a stag and torn to pieces by his own dogs, on Mount Cithoeron. (See "A Complete Latin-English Dictionary for the use of Junior Students", by John T. White, D. D. Oxon, Longmans, Green, and Company.)[63] And poor Diana! This nymph dashed about in partial deshabille—one breast out—brandishing a shield and a bow, though how she fired the latter while holding the former has never been satisfactorily explained. Some say that she "got her buck"—i.e. this Actaeon character in disguise.

(7) Then a serious note in that *"Because against the trunk is leaning a lance and a quiver, symbols of Diana"*. Sorry, Prof, but there is no quiver in any first-hand, 8 x 10 glossy print (of which I have three) of this picture. There is a straight thing extending from about midway up the main object to the ground right; but this is not a lance. It looks more than suspiciously like a taut wire or other cable and with a fairly obvious turn-buckle at the bottom end. And who ever (certainly not you, professor) said that the bloody thing was (is) a trunk; a trunk of what? Then, just what are Diana's symbols? A lance and a "trunk"? How about her bow and shield, or did you omit to mention those?

(8) *"Others believe it is in the pointed shape of the club of Hercules"*. We have spent months searching through every conceivable tome for some description of the shape of the club that some (and mostly in the Middle Ages) said this Hercules character carried. Nary even a mention of the damned thing, let alone of its shape. But we did stumble across some fanciful pictures, by fanciful latecomers, of this very fanciful and mythical character. Some of these showed him wielding a club *in his left hand*. (See my previous "THINGS" anent the Wudéwasa.[64]) This I find very significant as said device was always shown as a rough log with a lumpy head and somewhat cut down at the base for a handhold.

From then on, this communication goes off at a tangent. And this is where these "Alexandrian Mysteries" come in.

We're back to Zaitsev, the Bible, Charles Hapgood, and just about everybody else who has ever tried to make some real sense out of history. Alexandria, might we point out, was a cosmopolitan city on the southern shore of the Mediterranean, somewhat to the west of the delta of the Nile. At the time of the Emperor Augustus Caesar, this Graeco-Persian-Hebrew-Egyptian city was a seat of learning and the repository of nearly a thousand years of accumulated knowledge in the form of libraries and what can only be called laboratories. The knowledge stored in these indeed included "mysteries" or what appeared utterly mysterious to such brash yokels as Romans and especially to their besotted, nouveau-riche rulers. Further, these Latin ditch-diggers, having no real religion of their own, were completely overawed by both sissy Greek philosophers and more so by the age-old dynastic Egyptian hierarchies. "Sex" was a big deal in Rome, and Egypt's Isis very well fitted the bill. Anything *ex Africa*, to wit, in those days ex Egypt, was 'it'. And the Alexandrian stuff was "in" for a couple of centuries.

Objects similar to the rocket on its pad of which we are speaking have been found also in Livia's dining room. No wonder it is represented as a "great (tree) trunk supporting a circle on which hang(s) hunting trophies". We dug into this one and found that the only representation that has been published shows no less than sixteen "Ankhs" so depended. These are the sacred symbols of the "First-time People" whom the Egyptian priests revered. So, *"Here,* (there are indeed) *many* (similar things?) *which are common and belong to a group of Alexandrian mysteries . . . which are too much for us . . . mysteries."*

Well, they may be so for today's Roman scholars but we would opine that this is a pretty sad state of affairs. Here we have a perfectly clear, clean, and lucid picture of something that looks just like a rocket on its pad and everybody tries to tell us that it is either (a) a depiction of something that a mythical person called Diana or an even more diaphanous character called Hercules used, or (b) that it is a complete mystery which somebody is going to *try* to explain. And in the latter case they even go so far as to state that it is an "Alexandrian mystery".

No, much better that we spend our time investigating

said mysteries, rereading the Bible, and the maps of the ancient sea kings, and treat this Vyacheslav Zaitsev's pontifications a little more seriously. You don't have to believe anything you read in these works but just suppose for a moment that *their* theory *might* be right. In one fell swoop we would be rid of Diana, Hercules, and all the other mysteries and obtain a pretty clear-cut outlook on possibility. (I am not implying probability, please understand.) If there has been interference from outside by hominoid types throughout the ages they might well be said by the peasants to have descended in my beloved "Celestial Eggs". Further, they could indeed have caused all manner of mysteries. They might even have taught some yokel to paint, and told him to render into Caesar a valid record of a launching of one of their celestial eggs. This makes a heck of a lot more sense to me than *démodé* Diana, this Actaeon stag-person, and the old Abominable Snowman named Hercules. Think it over some time.

Part IV

MORE FUNNY THINGS

Chapter 11.

MECHANICAL DOWSING

EVERY COUNTRY-MAN, be he farmer, gardener, sylvi-culturalist, or professional botanist (and just about everybody in eighth grade) knows that the roots of plants, and particularly of trees, search out underground water supplies with the growing tips of their rootlets. Ditch-diggers and bulldozer operators are constantly amazed at the comparatively enormous distances that tree roots may probe horizontally before they turn down to find water. Nonetheless, it has not as yet been explained how they do this. Their search, moreover, is not random but directional and, as often as not, uni-directional.

This ability or capability appears to be inherent in the plant itself, though the stimulus—in this case standing or running water—comes from its environment and thus from "outside". Further, it appears to be primarily a function of the cells of the root system, as may be clearly demonstrated by using a "Y" cut from a root system alongside one taken from a branch, as is the custom among "professional" and all other dowsers to detect water. Try it some time; you will probably be most surprised.

Among animals, other than people, the exhibition of water-detection is more subtle, less obvious, and so far less known as to be almost *un*known. Yet, almost all animals display an ability both to go unerringly to surface water and/or to search from the surface. How they do this has neither been explained nor properly investigated. Take, for instance, the incredible swarms of animals, from kangaroos and emus to tiny marsupial-mice and insects, that congregate around the temporary shallow lakes that fill up from time to time right in the middle of the great Australian deserts. They come from miles—sometimes hundreds of miles—around, unerringly and immediately when these lakes suddenly fill up, often after years of dessication. Consider also what has been observed of other desert animals in other deserts, notably insects that have been observed meandering about, twiddling their antennae for hours before suddenly starting to dig or burrow furiously downwards. If you dig alongside them, you will almost invariably hit water, provided you go down deep enough. By the same token, jungle animals perform likewise—but *upwards!*

This may sound very startling, but it is seldom realized that in jungle areas, even with the highest mean annual rainfall, there are almost invariably long periods when no rain at all falls; and then, due to the guttering and run-off systems of the land-surface, which is caused by the torrential rains at other times, standing or running surface water is just as rare therein as in a desert. In fact, the only standing water available at all, as is only too well known to those who have been lost in true primary tropical forest during a dry season, is in holes halfway up the giant trees. The amazing thing is that all manner of animals congregate around such waterfilled trees—for they are often hollow like factory chimneys, and filled from ground-level to a hole where the first branches divide—but that these are not exclusively arboreal animals or even climbers! I have found quantities of large, ground-living toads that do not seem to be able to climb a one-foot log, and even some tortoises that seemingly can't climb at all, high up in trees that contain water. How do these sorts of animals detect this water? (How they get up there presents another conundrum.)

Now, some peoples have the same ability, and without using sticks or other devices. Notable are the Bushmen of Southwest Africa and the "Blackfellers" of Australia, both of whom have been properly observed in the act, and the results of these observations have been duly reported.[65] Somehow these desert peoples go to both temporary surface-water and to the locations of underground water just as unerringly as do the lesser animals. All kinds of suggestions have been put forward to explain this ability, but never to my knowledge that they may have a "built-in" dowsing apparatus. The average investigator feels safer when he suggests that the people follow animals, or that, in the case of the surface water, they can "smell" it as it is borne by winds even to great distances.

Now here are a large series of facts that have been known and accepted by just about everybody in the world for millenia but which are as yet totally unexplained, and about which nobody has even attempted to do anything.

Indeed there is an immense literature on plants *finding* water and how they absorb it, evaporate it, and so on, but nary a word about *how* they find it. There is some very fine observational reportage on both men and other animals having the same abilities, but again almost nothing on the "how." *Except* for one exception—and it is just that: namely, an exception.

Since time immemorial, it seems, it has been more or less universally accepted that certain people can find water under the surface of the land and usually through the intermediation of some device. It may surprise city-dwellers to know that practically nobody anywhere in the world outside of towns or cities would dream of going to the labour or expense of digging or drilling a well for water without calling in one of these chaps—called "witchers" or "dowsers". And I am not talking of countries like Pakistan where the government maintains a whole department for dowsing, but of our own country, Canada, western and eastern Europe and even Russia. What is more, the enterprise is indulged even within the cities themselves, though the fact is seldom publicized and the charges for it do not turn up on either prospectuses or cost-sheets of real-estate people, builders, or landlords.

It is quite useless for anybody to deny these facts, and it is even more stupid to try and decry them. The practice is here and it is here to stay, and it has always been with us. However, there is another side to the question, and it is here that we run into an appalling situation.

First, the main question is—as it should so rightly be—does the procedure work? On this score, humanity would seem to be divided into four parts, like Gaul: 50% who assert that it does work; 30% who neither know nor care; 10% who say they don't know but are willing to be convinced; and about 10% who assert, and often not only vociferously but most virulently, that it is all rubbish and, what is more, can *not* work. Most regretfully I have to say that the last are once again the scientists and those who claim to think scientifically. On this occasion, however, and very curiously, this lot does not include the technologists and more especially the technicians. In fact, the latter, while seldom saying anything about the matter, just go on as they have always done, employing the procedure in order to circumnavigate all manner of irksome problems like digging up acres of concrete flooring to find a single broken pipe.

Second, comes the question as to how people—and some people in particular—can find water underground. This is, of course, assuming that they can, and do so, and to the satisfaction of any who pay them money. This is where we begin to run into trouble. For centuries everybody in certain parts of the world firmly believed that swallows plunged into ponds in the fall and hibernated in the mud during the winter. A couple of centuries ago you might have been horsewhipped for denying this or (if you lived in Europe) for suggesting that they flew all the way to South Africa instead. So, just because more or less everybody has been satisfied that some people can find underground water, does not in any way mean that either they or anybody else *can* do so. The continued survival of the belief makes it highly unlikely that the whole thing is wishful thinking, some sort of hallucination, or trickery. The fact that people have paid money for this, and especially such purse-consious types as millionaires and governments, makes it even less likely. If anybody wants to suggest that it has all been pure luck since stone-age times, I suggest they come up with at least an hypothesis: the mathematicians would surely like to hear of any such.

So if the thing works, why in the blazes hasn't anybody done anything about finding out *how?* The answer is that quite a lot of people have, but most unfortunately until about two years ago nobody seems to have adopted a sensible, practical and scientific attitude or approach to the problem. During the past century this was probably due to the fact that the scientists stated flatly that no such procedure *could* be. This is a most curious state of affairs, particularly since their handmaidens, the technologists, were by no means as definite in their opinions. Nonetheless, this positive denial by "sciencedom" in view of the rather obvious fact that the procedure *does* work, led to the usual split. The public as a whole, and those most particularly interested in the matter either from an intellectual or monetary point of view, have just gone off on their own and conducted innumerable and massive experiments. Most of these efforts claim to be "scientific" and not a few have actually qualified for that designation, but one and all that I have ever heard of were stuck with the age-old notion that the ability to dowse is a purely human attribute.

These good people finally divided into two camps, which they themselves categorize as the mystical and the practical; and, at first, I thought the latter coincided with our outlook. However, I recently learned that it does not.[66] What they mean is simply that there are among dowsers two schools of thought; namely, that the procedure is wholly "psychic" as they call it, or that it is physical but operating through a human being as a machine. The notion that it could be a perfectly natural mechanical procedure which can operate entirely without human influence or presence had not been considered. And this brings me to the outcome of our contemplation of this fact, and the point where we felt compelled to do something about the matter.

We searched around for some experiments we might set up that might produce some valid leads to proper scientific investigation. It then immediately became apparent that the first thing required was an examination of the *physical* factors involved in the detection of or attraction to water, on the parts of both plants and animals, for, without some explanations of these "forces", or whatever you wish to call them, and which must manifestly exist, it was obviously useless to start trying to unravel the behaviour of such plants and animals. And it was here that we really got a surprise.

In initiating any novel search (or even, very often, *research*) you never know just where you are going to come out; the most troublesome aspect of any such endeavour is to keep on the beam and not go wandering off on any of the innumerable side-roads that invariably open up as one goes along. We have learned over the years that some of the best thinkers with the widest range of ideas, and the most "open minds" (though I abhor that term) are not scientists but technologists, and notably the engineers and gadgeteers.

On this occasion, however, I had cause to also call in representatives of a "breed" of which I have considerable suspicion; this is the psychological and other "mental" specialists: and this because everybody seems to insist that dowsing has a parapsychological basis, and that, to oversimplify the matter, the ability to dowse is exclusively the ability of the human subconscious or other "powers" of the psyche, or whatever you want to call the non-conscious or non-material side of a living entity. Not only have I always suspected this assertion, I have as near proof within our current logic that the very notion itself is rubbish for the simple reason that whatever the "power(s)" employed by the human, other animal, or plant-body may be, the effects they produce are physical, and are therefore not only susceptible to physical analysis, but must be studied on a physical basis. In fact, I do not see what, if anything, psychologists can contribute to *any* investigation of this sort. Nevertheless, we called some in even at the risk of their causing delays in the work and muddling the issue with their theories. The real surprise on this occasion came, however, from the engineering department, and it was a double surprise.

First, the whole direction of our investigation was given to us by one of them at the outset; and, secondly, our whole procedure from then on followed a line suggested by them and mostly handled by them. The results not only astonished but infuriated the psych-boys, and considerably distressed some of the "professional" dowsers, but, as we soon came to realize, they completely confirmed our contention that the whole business is purely physical and one that need have nothing to do with any living thing, human or otherwise.

That humans could play the part of a machine on occasion is beside the point and requires an entirely separate enquiry in which, I contend, we would run into just the same problem—that whatever effects are observed would still be physical, susceptible to physical analysis, and wholly dependent upon physical laws. What we recorded in our experiments, moreover, lends great weight to this assumption.

Now, the basis of proper scientific enquiry is that the results of experiments may be and can be duplicated, reduplicated, and reproduced elsewhere, at other times, and at the wish of other investigators. In this instance *we* reduplicated them many times and with new and varying witnesses, though we had to use the same location. However, so precise, definite, and simple were the results obtained, that we decided not to publish them until we could persuade some other groups—better qualified and using equivalent apparatus and as far as possible a similar set-up, but totally unknown to us—to run their own series of experiments.

When we decided to investigate this troublesome matter, we invited the following group to attend and assist both with ideas, practical implementation, supervision, and analysis. There were three biologists: one a teacher of general biology working on his thesis in micro-plant-physiology; a doctor of human pathology; and the author, acting as a straight zoologist. There were three engineers, two holding degrees in physics; an inspector of government arsenals; an electro-magnetics expert, owner of his own company making specialized electronic devices for the services; and a design engineer of top rank, who specialized in electronic circuitry and who moves from one large company to another in an advisory capacity to "get the bugs out of recalcitrant devices" as he put it. This man has also specialized in the electric circuitry of the human body and the new developments in the field of mental and corporeal interference with it by radio and other E.M.I. effects. There was also a teacher in the department of psychology at a well-known college, and a practicing psychologist. At one time or another two science writers and straight reporters were present. We also had four local citizens who made a practice of dowsing, and two of these—one of them a Town Clerk—practiced it professionally for well-diggers. Some dozen others witnessed the experiments from time to time. It was the first of the engineers who set us on our course, and by a statement made at the beginning of our first planning session.

The town clerk was widely known in the area for his ability to find water. He put on a demonstration for us before we sat down to the first meeting—finding, incidentally, water just where we finally had to dig a deep well three years later! First, he cut a "Y-twig" from one of our pear trees, and then demonstrated the difference between this and various woods. But then he happened to mention that he had found that a wire coat-hanger worked better than any twigs, even willows. This too he demonstrated, and it was while he was doing so that the engineer from the arsenal turned up. He is a quiet man and said nothing until we went into conference; then he opened up in not unscathing terms. The substance of what he said was as follows:

It is, he told us, something of a rarity to find a proper blue-print or plan of water or other pipes, or of power-lines laid under the thick concrete floors of arsenal buildings. However, he told us, his department, which is responsible for maintenance of such structures, long ago gave up the wearisome practice of digging up the floors to find the pipes. "All we do", he said, "is have somebody, or anybody, just walk back and forth with two 'Ls' tracing out the paths of all the buried lines to their inlets and outlets so that we can spot the one needing attention. Only then do we call in the drills and go right for the trouble spot". At first we thought he was joshing the town clerk; but he offered to demonstrate immediately. And this he did right outside the house after only about half an hour's preparation.

We have a workshop well stocked with supplies as well as tools, and from these he selected some lengths of copper, brass, iron, glass, and plastic tubing which he cut into four-inch lengths. Next, he selected as many kinds of heavy wires and rods as were available, and he had me light up a bunsen-burner in our lab and bend two glass rods into "Ls", with one tine seven- and the other five-inches long. Meantime, he similarly bent the wires and rods of various substances, one of which was heavy welding wire. We then tramped out to the front lawn, which runs from the front of the house at an angle of about twenty degrees to the road sixty feet away. There were two pipes buried to a depth of four feet under this lawn and running from the house, parallel, and directly down this slope to a well and a drain respectively. The first, when the pump in the house was at rest, of course, remained full of stationary water; the other pipe, which was also of iron, but of larger diameter, was either drained of all water or could be filled by turning on four faucets in the house. There was also a four-inch ceramic drainpipe into which water could be poured from a hose. Our engineer friend just walked slowly from right to left and back again from points A to B, holding the various sections of tubing upright in his clenched fists, but with matched pairs of "L" rods with their short tines in these tubes and the long ones pointing forward.

As he crossed the pipes these "Ls" moved in various ways—either both to the right; both to the left; towards each other, forwards and inwards until they crossed and then back again; backwards, until they pointed directly backwards or cross over the operator's wrists; and in various other combinations. What is more, they always did the same thing when they were passed over (a) the pipe full of standing water, (b) an empty pipe, (c) water flowing *up* a pipe, as to the pump, and (d) water flowing down to the drain; though the movements of the tines were, of course, different in each case. They performed exactly the same *with everybody!*

This demonstration shook-up everybody, notably the professional dowsers and psych-boys, the latter being really very annoyed indeed, though I have to admit that even they expressed grave doubts about their previous opinions quite early in the proceedings. I have to admit that I personally could hardly contain my glee as these preliminary results offered me an enormously simplified method for investigating the purely physical aspects of the matter. Nevertheless, the rest of that work-day, and much of the night, was taken up with discussion and not a little argument, during which all the old saws about the *human* influence were dragged out.

The group broke up and retired very late, and they all slept late the next day. I did not. I was out collecting materials as soon as the local stores opened so that, by the time the others reassembled, I had some construction work well under way. This consisted of two four-by-four uprights, sunk four feet into the ground and with their butts firmly anchored with large rocks before the holes were filled in. Then a horizontal wire—quarter-inch plain (not braided) telephone guide-wire—was stretched between the tops of the posts and pulled taut with heavy turn-buckles at either end, and these in turn were hooked to five-foot metal stakes driven into the hard ground at a forty-five degree angle. This wire ran exactly northeast to southwest. (Later, as a check, we moved it to run exactly north to south, but precisely the same effects were obtained—except for the angle the "Ls" subtended to the new line of travel).

From this wire we hung a balanced, light, wooden frame suspended from a small clockwork motor geared to a small pulley-wheel by two equalized belts. Below and to the front, pairs of tubes were held in slots in an almost upright position, and in these pairs of "Ls" were dropped just as they had been when hand-held. The tubes were tipped ever so slightly forward in order to keep the for-ward-pointing tines of the "Ls" from being blown or other-wise directed to either side by other "natural" forces. The house is in a mile-long, low valley, containing only one other building, a cinderblock, two-storey house a quarter of a mile down the road which runs down the gutter of this valley. Opposite the house, and on the other side of this road, is a steeply sloping hay-field. When the con-struction work was completed, I herded everybody about a hundred yards up this field, armed with several pairs of binoculars and a small telescope; and, when they were all set up, I wound up the clockwork motor, released it, and then ran like hell over the fence and up to join the others.

At first we ran the machine at very slow speed but, subsequently, at ever-increasing velocities. And, what do you know? The "L-rods" performed, and invariably, in exactly the same manner with this entirely mechanical set-up as they had done when hand-held. And, although we repeated this simple experiment a number of times and with as many variations as we could think of, even to changing the compass-orientation of the wire itself, we got the same results.

At first it might appear that the investigation gave conclusive results, but this is really far from the case; hence our desire to have as many others as possible try to reproduce these experiments in as similar conditions as possible. While it would seem to prove once and for all that dowsing—for water, that is (though it worked equally well for an air-filled iron pipe and an empty ceramic drain)—has nothing to do with human beings and looks like a purely natural physical performance, one has to take a number of other possible factors into account that are not immediately apparent and which are not currently allotted any status in scientific orthodoxy.

First, it is *possible* that, although no human beings were closely present while the device was at work, the construc-tion had been set up by humans, and by several who were specifically and in some cases intensely interested in the proceedings and their outcome. It is asserted by not a few today that man's "mind" can affect inanimate objects, and notably machines, and at a distance. However, there is a tendency, I have noticed, for those who believe that this is possible, to feel that people so influence objects more in accord with their wishes than contrary to such desires.

Should this be the case, any such theory would in this instance seem to lend considerable *negative* emphasis to acceptance of the notion that the performance was humanly controlled because the majority of those present were fervently wishing that the device would *not* perform by itself and without actual physical human contact.

Second, we cannot say for sure that a similar experiment conducted elsewhere and in only slightly different circumstances must give the same result. We have the funniest magnetic set-up at our place, such that compasses cannot be used at all, and one has to conduct surveys with a planetable, starting from fixed points on large-scale Coast & Geodetic Survey maps. I don't see why this should affect the movement of "L" rods made of various metals, glasses, and plastics, but stranger effects than that have turned up in the course of experimentation; and especially with natural "forces".

The psych-boys put up a valiant rearguard action to the very bitter end by thinking up all manner of other abstruse possibilities, ranging from good old mass-hallucination to Carl Jung's mass-subconscious, but I will not go into all of this here since none of the rest of us "buy" any of these abstrusities, and particularly in the face of anything so clear-cut as what we had observed. Curiously, however, the engineers were quite ready to accept the possibility of "mind control", though still insisting that the actions and reactions *must be regarded as purely physical* in the proper sense of that word. The fact that "Y" sticks and wires, and even "Ls" do also work with people (and, by the way, we intend to try it with a trained dog sometime) would seem to boost the theory that animals, in the first place, are only machines, and electrical ones at that.

But there is another side to this coin. What of the water and the iron? Here, the chemiphysicists were mostly with us in suggesting that both are surrounded by what are loosely called "force fields", though of just what forces none of them are willing to say. Some have plunked for electromagnetic fields, but most of them, plus the engineers to whom we have spoken, seem to feel otherwise. But none of them has as yet suggested just what other "force" might be involved.

It is obvious that something changes when water starts to move; and it changes in different ways according to how it moves. The metal alone presents still other problems; but that certain specific effects are—or appear to be—observed with irons of various amalgams it becomes much more acceptable that other metals could be detected by "dowsing", as is so constantly claimed. When it comes to finding lost jewels, and artifacts made of all manner of substances, we have nothing to say because we have neither witnessed the performance, nor have we experimented with such.

As a rule, I like to offer some conclusion to all mysteries even if this is of a speculative nature only. In this case I have none to offer because the investigation is not concluded, and I publish it now only for the reason stated at the outset of this chapter—that others should be persuaded if possible to reproduce what we observed or to disprove it in other circumstances. In the meantime, two things have happened.

First, a company concerned with appraisal of items, theories, and methods in the field of engineering in its widest sense, on behalf of the armed services amongst others, got in touch with us. One of their associates was responsible for bringing dowsing for underground tunnels, water channels, and mineral caches to the attention of the U. S. Marine Corp, which resulted in the use of this procedure by the armed services in Viet Nam which was rather widely publicized in 1968.[67] The executive with whom we held discussions came to us as a result of a brief mention of what I have described above in the quarterly journal of our society.[68] Being an engineer he concurred with our outlook, attitude, and principal objective. This is, first, to investigate and observe the purely natural phenomenon itself, without human influence or interference as far as possible. He further concurred in the notion that until this phenomenon is proven to exist—and some idea of how it works and what it is, is at least suggested—that it is best to leave all the other work, in which a human factor is involved, strictly alone.

Second, our adviser in the fields of geophysics and geomorphology, Professor George C. Kennedy of the Geomorphological Department of the University of California at Los Angeles, also pounced on the business and presented us with the first real conundrum.[69] Here indeed is a paradox, for it is a straight "how" question. It may be simply stated as follows.

If these ridiculous "Y"s and "L"s do work in arsenals, in hidden valleys, and just about everywhere else, why in the dickens don't the much more sensitive [quotes] "microbalances always work in all laboratories, if there is an unexplainable [i.e. unexplained?] force field which attracts certain objects?" Why indeed?

Chapter 12.

SSP VERSUS ESP[70]

WE ONCE MOORED our little schooner alongside a mudbank at the mouth of a river on the coast of Honduras while we did some repairs to the engine, and during this time we spent much time observing the hosts of little fiddler crabs that inhabited these flats. Our radio had gone dead, and our captain had taken it with him in the launch to a not too distant port for repairs, so that we were out of touch with the world. The weather had been bright and sparkling, but suddenly, late one morning, it became overcast, windless, intensely hot and depressing. In midafternoon the fiddler crabs went crazy.

I have seen some peculiar natural phenomena during my world-wide wanderings and I have witnessed several that at first appeared extraordinarily funny (in both senses of the word), but I had not until that time observed anything quite so ridiculous as this crustacean performance. All the males, with their big right claws carried before them, were milling hysterically about, herding the females or industriously digging them out of their water-filled burrows. Near the muddy water's edge the males formed a solid, massed phalanx, all facing landward, and they surged back and forth with every tiny incoming ripple.

The ceaseless, agitated and apparently pointless rushing hither-and-thither continued for about an hour while we watched in fascinated mystification, and then suddenly, as if at some unheard command, the waterside phalanx began to advance inland with measured tread and deadly determination, all waving their large claws before them. And as they went, in a great arc stretching as far both ways as we could see, they herded the disorganized masses before them. In a few minutes the whole vast army had disappeared underneath the stunted mangrove bushes to landward. We followed them cautiously, just keeping them in sight until dark, but their progress never faltered, although they had by then travelled almost half a mile.

At ten o'clock that night our old captain returned from the port with the radio and announced that a hurricane was approaching the coast. We immediately battened down, started up the engine and crept up the river. Shortly after midnight we caught up with the fiddler crabs. They were still going inland, but now in such untold numbers that the entire swampy ground seemed to be blanketed with them. We passed these hosts and chugged slowly and cautiously up the ever-narrowing river, finally tying up farther inland behind a dense stand of mangrove trees that topped our masts.

The crabs caught up with us next morning, but they did not pass us entirely. At four o'clock that afternoon the hurricane hit with blinding fury and, as is often the case in such affairs, the sea rose many feet and flooded the low coastal lands. The flood waters, however, only just reached the forest floor where we were anchored. How did the fiddler crabs know, more than twenty-four hours in advance, that a hurricane was coming, and how did they know exactly how far they had to travel inland to avoid the dangerous effects of its pounding frontal waves?

One explanation stems from the known fact that a hurricane pulls up the surface of the ocean over an immense area, often reaching far beyond the periphery of the circular wind itself. The waters thus sucked-up from all directions must come from the surface of the sea round about and, if this surface lies near a coast, it at first results in what appears to be an exceptionally low tide. Then, as the hurricane approaches, the dome of water itself reaches the coast and a great flood of sea water pours over the land in what is often, but quite erroneously, called a tidal wave.[71]

It has been suggested that the fiddler crabs, which live in shallow, water-filled holes just above the normal tide level, are highly sensitive to these unusual fluctuations of water level, the first signs of which are far too slight for us to appreciate. However, this does not explain either their reaction or their apparent ability to take exactly the required evasive action. Possibly, and perhaps more probably, they, like certain other animals we will mention, possess some special senses or other mechanisms for measuring the barometric pressure of the air, which is profoundly affected by the approach of hurricanes or other cyclonic storms, and often while they are still at great distances.

That animals may possess such senses can no longer be denied, for in the past two decades we have discovered all manner of previously unrecognized and unsuspected sense organs and measuring devices on the bodies of animals of all kinds. Many of these not only look like some of our own most advanced devices but many are now known actually to function upon the same mechanical principles, while others prove to be activated by forms of energy that we have only just recently discovered for ourselves. For instance, it is now well known that the complicated flaps of skin found around the nostrils of some bats, and certain strange structures in their ears, are for the projection and reception of sound waves of ultra-high frequency upon the principles we now call sonar. The bats emit bursts of sound of frequencies up to 32,000 per second, but for intermittent periods of as little as a two-hundredth of a second each. These air-borne waves bounce back from obstacles ahead of the bat when it is in flight, and are picked up by the supersensitive ears of the animal in the period of silence between the bursts of sound. So sensitive are their auditory devices that the animals can invariably alter course in time to avoid the obstacles. Sonar, and even the whole concept of supersonics, was unknown to us until, comparatively speaking, a few years ago, yet bats have been using devices functioning upon these principles for millions of years.

A list of the mechanisms which may be called *sense organs* that have now been identified on animals is not only enormous but positively startling in other respects. First, we don't know what most of them are, or how they work, or for what purposes they have been developed. Secondly, many of them appear to have a dual or triple purpose, and thirdly, some appear to function in fields of which we as yet know nothing apart from the fact that they exist—like the electromagnetic analysis of smells. Finally, it is currently being discovered that there is considerable confusion over the classification of the recognized senses *per se*. In this field it appears that lack of knowledge on our part and much oversimplification are to blame.

It is obvious that a Roman senator standing on a fish, known as an "electric ray," in the hope of alleviating his rheumatism, would not understand how the fish worked because he had no concept of the principles of electro-magnetism. We in turn may perhaps be excused for our complete failure to understand how fiddler crabs can fore-tell cyclonic storms, for we don't seem to have any inkling of the field or fields in which any mechanism functions that they may have. But we are certainly making matters unduly hard for ourselves when we insist that there are only five senses, and that sound, for instance, is invariably air-borne, and can be heard only with ears.

Actually we ourselves possess many more than five sen-ses, and some authorities claim at least two dozen for us. As examples which can be readily appreciated, consider your own sense of gravity (balance), dessication (thirst), electromagnetic flux (shock), or infrared radiations—that is, radiated, as opposed to conducted, heat. Moreover, our inherent concepts of sight, hearing, touch, taste and smell are founded on our rather limited activities in only one of several possible major environments—, in the air at about sea level.

Deep-sea fish and parasitic tapeworms live in complete-ly different worlds. The former may or may not see, according to whether they have eyes; the latter apparently do not, but both apparently "hear", although they lack ears—at least both respond to air-or water-borne sounds or vibrations. A fish accomplishes this by means of lines of mucus-filled pits along its flanks and head, which are supplied with nerves leading to that part of the brain which is connected with the organs used for hearing by other animals. The tapeworm apparently feels the impulse through its skin all over its body. In either case, are we to call this function "hearing" or "touch"?

One of the most valuable groups of animals, from the scientific point of view, is the lesser whales, which include dolphins of all kinds and porpoises. Those that inhabit tropical seas are most in demand because several of them, like the Pigmy Sperm whale, have never been seen alive. For years I spent fruitless hours cruising in likely waters, hoping for a chance at these elusive creatures.

Then one day in line of duty during World War II, I had occasion to arrest a professional shark-fisher on suspicion of enemy affiliations—quite unfounded, as it turned out. During the course of interrogating him, I happened to ask what he used as bait to catch the sharks, and when he told me dolphins, I almost jumped out of my chair. But when I asked him how he caught the dolphins, I actually did so, because he told me that he simply called them to his boat by hammering on its hull. Of course, I didn't believe him, but as soon as I could sneak away from official wartime duties I took our schooner out into the blue water and, when nobody was looking, started tapping on her hull. And sure enough a school of dolphins appeared almost immediately. Since then I have done this dozens of times and, provided one is in dolphin waters, it seems never to fail.

The explanation, although known to fishermen since approximately 3000 B.C. in the Mediterranean, was initially given by scientists working on underwater sound at Woods Hole Oceanographic Institute, in Massachusetts. They found that the ocean below the aerial uproar of the waves is a nightmarish cacophony of noises composed of grunts, moans, screams, wolf whistles, coughs, and ghastly yells, against an almost continuous background of what radio technicians call "grass", caused by the snapping of pincers by countless millions of various kinds of shrimps. What is more, if you float with your ears under water on a fairly still day some yards offshore along almost any of our coasts, you will hear some of these sounds quite clearly. Most common are sharp clicks like the striking together of two flints, but sometimes you will hear a doleful lowing not unlike that of a distressed cow. This is one of the calls of a dolphin. Apparently these strange water mammals, although having ear holes only about the size of a pencil lead, have a whole repertoire of sounds by which they communicate, and tapping with a hammer on the wooden hull of a boat for some reason positively intrigues them—at least in certain warm tropical seas.[72]

But the world of sound is not the only one where mysteries abound. It had been thought until very recently that man alone had harnessed electromagnetic forces and put them to work, but then came a fish known as *Gymnarchus niloticus,* from the Nile, as its name implies, and shaped like a compressed eel.[73] Instead of having a normal, fishy tail, its body terminates in a slender, feeler-like, fleshy finger. This extraordinary animal lives in muddy waters among reeds and other snags, and when scared it darts backward at great speed, with enormous agility and always without running into anything. Now it has been discovered that it has means of creating and storing electricity and of discharging it into the water in controlled bursts. What is more, it can pick up, or receive, these impulses either from others of its kind or from its own broadcasting by reflection from solid objects—and apparently through its peculiar, fingerlike tail or by the lines of mucus-filled pits along its flanks. Thus it employs its electromagnetic energy for an efficient form of underwater radar, or radio location, just as we do, broadcasting expanding spheres of electrical waves in all directions and picking up any that are reflected from particular points by obstacles. Somehow it manages to interpret these reflections, just as bats do with air-borne waves, in time to alter its course and so avoid running into things when darting backward, even in muddy water at night.

It is a somewhat disturbing thought that a rather dismal fish has for millions of years been using a device which we only discovered in the nick of time to help save our side in WW II. What other things may animals have "discovered", before even the first man walked this earth, which we still do not even suspect?

The range of possibility appears to be almost limitless. The Parapsychology Laboratory at Duke University, under the able guidance of Prof. J. B. Rhine, once became interested in what is called the homing instinct of animals. This has been a sore subject among zoologists for many years and one in which little if any real progress has yet been made. The most obvious example is that of homing pigeons whose almost infallible ability in this respect has been known for centuries. That these birds can find their way home from great distances even if carried there in closed containers cannot be denied, but how they do it has not been completely explained. They have been followed in airplanes, and although observed to start off by flying in an ever-expanding spiral until they apparently orientate themselves, the method they use for their precise navigation is still under investigation.

Various suggestions have been made, notably something called the Coriolis Effect, which is the minute shove to the west that everything is under on the surface of the earth due to its west-to-east spin. Then it was supposed that pigeons have some mechanism by which they can divine the lines of magnetic force that envelop our planet. However, no practical experiment so far devised has been able to prove that the birds can sense or use either force. When small magnets, designed to counteract or upset the normal earth magnetism, were attached to their wings, the birds with only one magnet in place found their way home just as readily as those carrying two or none. More recent studies seem to indicate that they, like the Horseshoe Crab described below, use the polarization of sunlight. Whether this is the method used by other animals is not known, but it has been shown that gulls, pelicans, gannets, and other birds, as well as elephants, bats, fish, lobsters and numerous other animals have just as strong homing instincts.

Then there is the whole question of seasonal migration, which is doubly perplexing because not only do numerous birds and other animals find their way unerringly, year in and year out, over distances that sometimes, as in the case of the arctic tern, exceed the circumference of the earth, but their young sometimes do so alone unguided in their first year.[74] Should these animals be able to perform only in daylight, we might have an explanation. Certainly pigeons and bats do just as well at night, as do some lobsters which operate in perpetual darkness and elephants retain such knowledge over enormous periods of time—in fact, up to ten years.

Researchers on honeybees and the horseshoe crab, and that ridiculous hang-over from before the age of the dinosaurs found on our Eastern seaboard, have demonstrated at least one way by which some animals may orientate themselves provided there is sunlight. The famous Austrian scientist, Prof. Karl von Frische,[75] whose work on bees has been so widely publicized, opened a whole new world of possibility to those who study the behaviour of animals. He demonstrated that the honeybee not only indicates the presence, direction and distance of suitable pollen and nectar to other members of its hive by executing strange little geometrical dances comprehensible to its fellows, but also that it orientates itself by a most complex compass, built into its head in the form of its compound-faceted eyes, which are sensitive to the degree of the polarity of sunlight. To reduce this almost to the point of oversimplification, it should be explained that the waves of light streaming from the sun in all directions naturally travel directly outward. Thus they may be said to travel in a straight line, or in one direction. Now, as the earth revolves, an animal on its surface views this direction from a different angle as the sun rises and then sets.

The bee, simply by taking a single glance at any bit of the sky in daylight, can interpret this angle immediately and thus determine the position of the sun, the time of day, and its position relative to the hive or the place where the food is. This intelligence is then made known to other bees via the medium of the tail-wagging dances.

The work on horseshoe crabs was carried out by Prof. Talbot H. Waterman, of Yale's Osborn Zoological Laboratory.[76] He has shown that these lowly animals can also detect the position of the sun, even if they cannot see it, by the degree of polarity or angle of vibration of its light in the sky. The Navy was sufficiently interested in this discovery to back his researches, because they could provide us with an efficient compass for the months of twilight navigation near the poles where ordinary magnetic compasses are useless, the sun is below the horizon, and the stars cannot be seen. Yet the horseshoe crab has been using the polarity of sunlight for some hundreds-of-millions-of-years, whereas we became aware of this basic principle of light only during the last century. But, as I have said, there seems to be no limit to the possibilities of animal senses.

It was not so long ago that we discovered that what we call light, or the visible band, extends apparently indefinitely both beyond the violet and the red edges of the spectrum, though our eyes cannot see beyond those limits. Now it is being realized, and with ever-increasing frequency, that there are many animals which can detect waves beyond these limits and which apparently can sometimes actually see by them.

Mammals—that is to say animals with hair that suckle their young—are, as we all know, warm-blooded and maintain a constant internal temperature. Thus, on cool nights, they will radiate a certain amount of heat. Certain snakes (known as the pit vipers) have on the sides of their muzzles and in front of their eyes, flask-shaped hollows or pitlike organs which are highly sensitive to these heat or infrared radiations, and these reptiles hunt their mammalian food by using these organs as direction-finders that lead them unerringly to small, warm-blooded prey. However, certain owls that also hunt small mammals, but in pitch-darkness and usually over fields of tall, matted grass, are believed to make a living by a different application of the same principle. According to at least one authority,[77] their great eyes are sensitive to these infrared heat rays, so that they actually "see" the passing of a little, warm field mouse as an appreciable streak against the tangle of cool grasses, thus leading them to make a satisfactory strike.

This, though marvelous, is at least understandable, once one has grasped the idea that only a very limited range of all wave lengths, as they are popularly called, are detectable by our human eyes, and that other animals can have similar organs with a much wider range of vision. The matter becomes much more amazing, however, when we read the results of work done upon certain moths that mate after dark.

The males find their way unerringly over very considerable distances in total darkness and regardless of wind direction, to the females of their own species, which appear to sit complacently doing nothing. This has been an old puzzle to entomologists, but then a spectroscopist entered the field and discovered that the females are really broadcasting a mating-call over infrared wavelengths. Not only was the female found to be some eleven degrees warmer than her surroundings, but it was also discovered that her heat was given off in a complex pattern of varying frequencies with fluctuating peaks of intensity in different wavelengths. Further, the males bear immense, elaborate antennae with plumes of minute, subdivided hairs. The scientists discovered that these hairs varied in length by a certain fixed amount or by multiples of that amount, and that this was within the range of variation of the females' broadcasting frequencies, all of which means— though it may be clear only to an electronics engineer— that the male moth can pick up the female mating-broadcasts with its antennae.

We, with our limited sense range, might well be led to believe that the male moth—by some mysterious means— predicts the exact position its mate will be occupying, or the owl that of its quarry, when in reality they are led to them in a manner that is really no more complex than our ability to tune in a radio set or find our way through a lighted room. Yet these accomplishments, though commonplace to us, are really very miraculous if one comes to analyze them.

Perhaps the ability of birds to predict the weather is founded on no more mysterious factors than that of the dolphins, which respond to a gentle tapping noise, but one must admit that until we have discovered the means by which they do so, their actions may on occasion seem utterly incomprehensible, uncanny, and altogether out of this world. For instance, take the case of the European Swift.[78]

These birds winter in South Africa, but nest in Northern Europe in the spring and then spend the summer in these far-northern latitudes. They feed exclusively on flying insects which they catch on the wing, and they are believed to spend their whole lives in the air, except when nesting. Finnish ornithologists have published a weird account of their actions at the approach of summer cyclones from the North Atlantic area. All the birds, it appears, invariably leave well in advance of these storms and fly hundreds of miles either to the south or north to get away from the bad weather, during which time all their essential insect food is grounded. What is more, it has been found that their tiny, naked, helpless young, which naturally have to be left behind, unprotected in the open nests, immediately go into temporary hibernation—behaviour they never adopt when the parents are around, even if they are left alone for long periods.

How do these birds know several days in advance that a cyclonic storm is coming, and how do they then know exactly the only two possible directions in which to fly in order to escape the fury of the storm and the starvation in which it would result? We do not know, but we may have found a clue in the study of bird "fairs", which are among the most extraordinary phenomena in nature.

Many species of sea birds (notably those which gain their living on the open oceans throughout most of the year) like the flightless penguins, certain petrels or sea pigeons and the tropical boobies, assemble at special points year after year to lay their eggs and rear their young. We once witnessed such a gathering on a tiny island in the Caribbean to which vast hosts of boobies came from near and far. The peculiar thing about this particular fair was that these same birds had regular roosts on other widely scattered islands which they returned to every night throughout the rest of the year, but they did not nest there, and all apparently congregated at this one island only at this one season, and all arrived within about two days, after which only a few old birds or those in bad condition straggled in alone, sometimes to fall exhausted on the beach.

When we landed on the island, which is off the tip of Cape Gracias a Dios, there were only half a dozen boobies fishing about in the surrounding waters. Nothing happened for three days. Then, shortly after dawn, our old skipper, who had brought us to see this strange sight, called us on deck and indicated what appeared to be a dense, low mist on the horizon to the east. Seen through glasses in the dim light, this mass, which stretched throughout an arc of about 100°, was resolved into an oncoming army of birds, all planing and dipping over the swell. Half an hour later the advance guard arrived, circled the island and then settled down amid raucous cries and a cloud of feathers. The birds didn't even bother to manoeuvre properly, but banged into one another and fought for space on the ground.

They continued piling in all that day in huge flights, coming from all points of the compass, and we heard more armies arriving during the night. By next morning there was hardly standing room on the island, and egg laying was already on a mass-production basis. Smaller groups continued to come in all day and night, but by next morning only single birds were to be seen struggling in from far afield while the air around us was tortured with screaming, whirling thousands.

What signal had brought all these multitudes from the far reaches of the Caribbean, and perhaps from the Atlantic beyond, to this paltry, overcrowded little island? By what sense did they pick up the signal or with what mechanism did they act upon it? It is now the predominant opinion among those who have studied this phenomenon that the stimulus comes from inside the animals themselves and is connected with the seasonal nesting and egg-laying urge. But how they judge their individual distances from the nesting island so accurately that they all arrive there virtually at the same time, though they may start from ten, one hundred, or even one thousand miles away, is still completely unexplained. Similarly, while it is obvious that the swifts must have some built-in device that is sensitive to oncoming cyclones, we still don't know what part of the body houses this mechanism or how it produces one type of reaction in the adult birds and quite a different one among the nestlings.

The trouble, from our point of view, is probably that our technology has, so far, developed only to a point where comparatively short-range prediction is possible, as in sonar, radar, and heat detection. Our current difficulties with weather predictions are notorious, but then we have only been around for about one million years, while most other animals have had various multiples of this time in which to develop methods for interpreting their environment and its future possibilities. Some of these methods are still unknown to us, and we may not yet even suspect the existence of the principles upon which they function.

Examples of such accomplishments by animals that are unexplained as yet and which seem to us currently both inexplicable and uncanny, could be related almost *ad infinitum*. The same may, in a way, be said of ourselves. Throughout history certain individuals have been alleged to have "super-sensory" powers and abilities, and most often of detection of one kind or another, but it was not until comparatively recently that anybody tried to investigate these matters scientifically. They, like the famous Dr. J. B. Rhine, started with the simplest manifestations they could find—card-calling, for instance—and they obtained some results that simply could not be attributed to either chance or cheating. Nobody took a particularly keen view of these findings and they are still being hotly debated.

These investigations were most unfortunately dubbed "parapsychological"; meaning *para*, like; *psych* which actually means "mind," "soul", or "understanding"; and *logos*, the study of. There could hardly have been a more unfortunate choice. Psychology purports to be the study of the "intellectual" or thinking behavior of animate objects. In practice, it is divided into an objective study which is entirely material and concerns itself with practical behaviour, and *is* a science, called ethology, and a purely subjective art which purports to catalogue, analyze, and interpret the mental or non-material aspects of such behavior—if there are such. In recent years, this art has presumed to make claims to be able to influence and direct such so-called mental behavior. This is extremely dubious.

Extrasensory perception has nothing whatsoever to do with this psychology. It concerns itself—or should do—entirely with practical, physical and material manifestations of the behavior of animals—and plants we should add. In fact, what the ESP people are actually doing is endeavouring to break through into the *super*-sensory aspects of ethology. We don't need any weird mental quirks to explain the things they observe; at least, not until we have thoroughly investigated all the definable mechanical senses of all animals, and decide—probably quite erroneously—that we have come to the end of all the possibilities. And, during such a process we might well, and could perhaps quite probably, find the clue as to how we can call cards across the Atlantic, predict the future and dredge up the past—time being what it might be!

Chapter 13.

AN HALLUCINATION?[79]

FOR SOME YEARS NOW—in fact for some centuries—people have been talking about something called "mass hallucination". This has always puzzled me. I have read all that I have been able to find about it, and I have talked to many prominent people in the fields of the mind sciences, but I'm still puzzled. I'm afraid I still don't know either what it is or just what it is supposed to be. I have learned even less of how it is supposed to work. So let me tell you a story.

Lo these many years ago, now I come to reckon it, my wife and I, and a very dear friend and then associate, had a most extraordinary experience. The experience itself was a roaring bore and quite troublesome but it had overtones or undertones that, on later reflection, appeared to be quite weird. I'm not given to this kind of stuff and I have not, until now, liked to talk about it, but I feel that I am old enough to come out with it and let whatever chips there might be fall all over the lot. (And, if anybody can get more cliches into one sentence than that I'll offer them a job in the promotional field!) But, to be serious.

I have never, as I said above, been interested in, nor

have I ever studied, what is commonly called the occult. Let me make myself quite clear on this point. What I say does not mean that I deny the whole or any part of this field of interest nor that I have ever consciously denigrated it. It is just that I have only one life to lead (that I know of), and I've been far too busy trying to catch up with the more pragmatic facts of it. However, I must admit, on mature consideration, to having given a few nasty sneers at this thing called "mass hallucination". Now I'm not so sure, and I'd like to try and make restitution for any possible impertinence.

Other fields of pure science in which I have recently become involved have shown me that "there is more to it than that"—*that* being what we call reality. Not only are there things going on that our (now) couple of dozen senses cannot pick up, but there is also a whole vast world which, whether or not it is linked to the world of so-called reality that we live in, seems to become apparent only through what we call *The Mind*.

This immediately brings up the question: "What is a mind?" We don't know, but it appears to be a (subjective) concept of something connected with a purely physical (objective) something called a brain. There is now doubt about even this if some medical histories are correct because, while the physical brain is undoubtedly a sort of central switchbox, it may not be the sole seat of this interpretive thing called "the mind". The whole organism may participate, or even be required, to make a "mind" function. (Note: the Russians have been reported to have cut dogs' heads off at superspeed and then stuck them back on again; and, it is alleged that they may have swapped heads and bodies! Then there's the fellow who wrote a will the night before he died in a New York hospital whose body—*allegedly*, though I don't have any references—on autopsy showed only half a cupful of dirty gray water in his skull. You, dear readers, can take that one from there.) But, back to my story.

My wife and I and my loyal assistant, named Frederick G. Allsop (lately in charge of the United States Rubber Company's interests in the West Indies), were living in a small "native" village named Pont Beudet in Haiti. This was in the middle of the great plain that separates the two huge mountain chains of the island of Hispaniola, points west, and runs back to a large freshwater lake named

Azuey. Our profession was biological survey, and we were collecting the small-life of the area. We lived very happily and comfortably in a series of small houses constructed of mud and wattle with thatched roofs in an honest-to-goodness compound just like you see in old movies. We had one local lad working for us, and a magnificent older lady known everywhere simply as "Margo" who took care of our domestic needs in conjunction with my wife. But Margo was a person apart.

You may have heard a lot of nonsense about "Voodoo" in Haiti. First of all, the correct way of saying this, is *vaudun,* with an emphasis on the terminal *-un.* Secondly, it is not some kind of ghastly, black-magical, phoney semi-religion, as it has almost invariably been made out to be by sensationalists and mere travelers. Vaudun is nothing more than the permissible residue of a number of African animistic concepts that either coincided with the precepts of the Roman Catholic Church or did not. Indeed, there are aspects of vaudun that do not so coincide but, nonetheless, the peasantry of Haiti have continued to reproduce them on traditional grounds and no harm has been done. (May I make it clear that the whole matter of black-magic, and "zombies", and all that tosh, have nothing to do with this.)

The point I wish to make is that our beloved Margo was what is called in Haiti a "Mamm'an Celie" (as far as I can transpose the term); that is, a "guider" of tradition, all the way from village dances to the less understood aspects of vaudun. I suppose stupid, or even sensible, "whites" from outside would call her a priestess; and, in a way, they would be right, for she ministered to her flock just like the priestesses of old. She was a magnificent-looking woman, and one of great compassion. For some reason unknown to me she adopted my wife. And I mean adopted. So, on with the next part of the story.

One beautiful evening the three of us—my wife, my assistant, and I—decided to take a drive up the old road to Lake Azuey. We had two hours to go before the descent of the very prompt tropical sunset but, since we had an ancient Rolls-Royce and nothing to do, we just set off with a little bag to collect freshwater snails. We were all wearing sandals without socks as is the custom; my wife wore a dress, I think; Fred, a pair of pants and a loose shirt; and I, a set of pyjamas. We were not a very impressive entourage but in the tropics, who cares?

We drove along the north road, east, and came to the beautiful lake, though there wasn't much to see and darned few freshwater snails to collect. Then, like bloody idiots, we decided to cut south via an old dirt road originally built by the U.S. Marines (when they occupied Haiti in early 1930) to the south road and that's where we made our mistake.

Haiti is a very strange country. The great plain is a dry, dusty, cactus-strewn mess, but on it are a number of very old sugar-cane plantations and other things. In olden (French colonial) times, these were watered or irrigated by little canals and ditches that brought refreshment from the mountains to north and south—and mostly from the south. These ditches still exist, and water still flows down them but they have been neglected so that at "passes" for oxen, and other vehicles, they have burst their bounds and formed muddy ponds that in many cases are virtual morasses.

In driving south we hit several of these, but our old and powerful car just smashed through them until we came to one that we misjudged . . . and . . . 'GLUPP' . . . down we went, hub-high in a gooey mass of mud.

So what do you do, about sundown, forty miles from anywhere, in Haiti, wearing pyjamas and sandals, without food or water, with an ancient Rolls-Royce stuck in the mud and a small bag containing bottles to collect freshwater snails? Ladies and gentlemen: you do one of two things. Either you sit and nothing happens—and, in Haiti, *nothing* happens—or you walk. We chose to do the latter; and this is where my story really gets going.

We walked; oh, dear God, but *did* we walk! It got dark, and the cactuses "developed" spines, and a fellow on a horse came roaring at us, in pitch-darkness before the moon came up, out of nowhere, and we all dived for said cactuses. Then we walked some more.

At this point, I should make it clear that we were, or thought we were, walking due south. Then the moon came up. I have always "dug" the Moon, and for more reasons than one. On that occasion, it came gloriously up over the mountains, round, clear and luminous and in a matter of minutes it lighted our way. And that's when we first realized that we had strayed out into the middle of the plain. Actually it was that damned horseman who caused us to lose the so-called road in the pitch blackness. But we stumbled on.

Then, quite suddenly we saw looming before us the ruins of an old sugar-mill. It was deserted and a bit eerie but it had a huge stone water-trough filled with clear water and a profuse growth of green algae. We looked at each other and then at the water, and suddenly my wife gave a sort of gurgle and pointed. She is an entomologist of a rather specialized kind and she had spotted mosquito larvae in the water; and that, she contended, meant it was drinkable since there were no people around. So we drank; and why we didn't empty that tank I don't know. We looked for an old bottle or gourd or anything else to carry some more with us but the place was stripped and very old. An empty bottle is a valuable item in the Haitian countryside. So we started out again angling toward the southern mountains now clearly visible through the tangle of cactuses, for we knew that the other road lay along their base.

It was an incredibly hot night and the air was as dry as the parched ground. I have no idea how long we walked but eventually we hit the road and turned right towards Port-au-Prince and the main road north from it on which we lived. Then things began to happen.

Haiti is a very strange country. Its population is vast, its economy tragic. Quite apart from vaudun which is, as I have said, a residue of legitimate and traditional African animism, it is superstition-ridden to the *nth* degree. Further, while there is also a traditional hatred by all strata of society (by color) for the next and all lighter-skinned strata above, it does not matter if you are "coal-black"; you still won't be accepted by your compères if you are a foreigner. I have never been in a country, and I have been in most, where xenophobia is so ingrained and pronounced. Then again everybody believes in ghosts of all kinds.

Now here were two very white men and a very light-complexioned woman, all wearing 'foreign' clothes, stumbling along a dark road after midnight. This is not done in Haiti, and it is not good, because the Haitian peasants walk all night, taking their small loads of goods to market. They walk in clutches in the middle of the road and they babble and sing all the time to keep away or appease the ghosts or *chumbis*. Of course, we ran into a gang almost immediately, and pandemonium broke loose.

Luckily, this first lot were all women because almost all the men carry their machetes with them and, if a ghost turns out to be solid and they are cornered they will take a very effective swipe at it. And a Haitian-type machete wielded by a Haitian can cleave you into two halves almost any which way. Luckily also, Fred Allsop had lived in the country for twelve years and spoke Haitian Creole fluently *and* with all the peasant jargon. He started yelling, and kept it up. I asked him later what he had yelled and he told me he twitted them for mistaking three silly white people for ghosts. We also started singing as we tramped along, and, taking our cue from Fred who also knew all their village songs—with current jokes—we joined in. Then a pair of headlights appeared away ahead.

A car out at that time of night in Haiti in those days was really an oddity and so had to be something official or at least frightfully important. So I was determined to stop it, and I stood in the middle of the road—at peril of death, knowing Haitian drivers—waving my pyjama top, and refused to budge. My wife screamed but the car stopped about two feet in front of me, and a lot of people scrambled out cursing in three languages. And, of all things, one was an American doctor. It transpired that a man had cut his foot off with an axe at a turpentine operation way up in the pine forests and the police at the nearest point had radioed for help.

No, the doctor insisted, he had no room for us, and he could not help us but, if we were still on the road when he came back—and we still had about thirty miles to go he told us—he would let us cling to the back of the truck. So away he went, and we stumbled on again. And it was just after the headlights had vanished behind us that it happened.

The road was perfectly straight, dust-covered, without side ditches—just bare earth running away among the cactuses and low thorn scrub not more than ten feet tall. Fred was far in front in case we caught up with a party of Haitians they were almost all going our way), my wife was in the middle, and I was close on her heels for her safety's sake. We were not just tired, we were exhausted; but despite the truck that we knew was now behind us, we wanted to get off that plain before the sun came up.

You don't know that plain, or just what the tropical sun can do to it. In such circumstances, one gets into a sort of "swing", both physically and mentally as any traveler who has been really lost will affirm. If you are sensible, you stop "thinking" if you can—and it *can* be done.

Then, suddenly, on looking up from the dusty ground I perceived absolutely clearly in the now brilliant moonlight, *and casting shadows appropriate to their positions*, three-storied houses of various shapes and sizes lining both sides of the road. These houses hung out over the road, which suddenly appeared to be muddy with patches of large cobblestones. The houses were of (I would say) about the Elizabethan period of England, but for some reason, I *knew* they were in Paris! They had pent roofs, some with dormer windows, gables, timbered porticos, and small windows with tiny leaded panes. Here and there, there were dull reddish lights burning behind them, as if from candles. There were iron-frame lanterns hanging from timbers jutting from some houses and they were all swaying together as if in a wind, but there was not the faintest movement of air about us. I could go on and on describing this scene as it was so vivid: in fact, I could *draw* it. But this is not the main point.

I was marveling at this, and looking about me, when my wife came to a dead stop and gave a gasp. I ran smack into her. Then she went speechless for a time while I begged to know what was wrong. Finally she took my hand and, pointing, described to me *exactly what I was seeing*. At which point *I* became speechless.

Finally pulling myself together, I blurted out something like "What do you think's happened?" but my wife's reply startled me even more. I remember it only too well: she said, "How did we get to *Paris* five hundred years ago?"

We stood marveling at what we apparently *both* now saw, picking out individual items and pointing, questioning each other as to details, and so forth. Curiously, we found ourselves swaying back and forth and began to feel very weak, so I called out to Fred, whose white shirt was fast disappearing ahead.

I don't quite remember what happened then but we tried to run toward him and, feeling dizzy, sat down on what we were *convinced* was a tall, rough curbstone. Fred came running back asking what was wrong but at first we did not know what to say. He was the "keeper" of the cigarettes, of which we had about half a dozen left, and he sat down beside us and gave us each one. By the time the flame from his lighter had cleared from my eyes, so had fifteenth-century Paris, and there was nothing before me but the endless and damned thorn bushes and cactus and bare earth. My wife also "came back" after looking into the flame. Fred had seen nothing, and was completely mystified by our subsequent babble; but he was not skeptical and insisted that we just sit and wait for the truck which he felt confident would come back that night.

It did, about an hour later. We climbed aboard and in half an hour we were at the doctor's house where he dropped off his chauffeur to drive us home in his own car, while he went on to the hospital with the truck. But that wasn't all. Oh dear me no!

On account of the nature of our work and the habits and customs of the local people who worked for us, our household had been run for many weeks on a most precise schedule. Meals were served on the dot but there were times when the three of us went into the capital, Port-au-Prince, or to see friends, and, there being no telephones then, we just did not come home to dinner. In such cases, Margo and her staff waited till 7:00 p.m. precisely, and then cleared off the table, took the hot food home to their families, and set the houselights for the night. I wish to emphasize that this procedure had been invariable for weeks.

So what do we find when we get home? The whole compound is a blaze of lanterns with people everywhere. We stagger in and Margo grabs my wife and whips her into the bedroom where there is a large bowl of hot water on the floor in which to have her feet washed. Lesser personages are scurrying in and out of the kitchen house with a lavish, steaming-hot meal. My "head man" had two tubs of hot water ready in the washhouse for Fred and me, and clean pyjamas laid out. But nobody says anything. Nor would they that night. We were stuffed with food and pushed into bed, and the lights went out though the dawn was just breaking.

The next day, I sort of sidled up to Margo—she tolerated me only because I was my wife's chosen man—and tried tactfully to get the clue. News travels fast in Haiti. There was that damned galloping horseman. And there were *drums*. We heard them throbbing throughout the night as they always do, but they seemed to be just village dances. "Talking" or communication-drumming is different, as I knew so well from Africa. But, given all of these, just how—may I ask—did our gang know exactly *when* we would get home, and *if* we would, to the point of having the food and bath water at just the right temperature. After all, the truck might not have come back; we could have stayed with the doctor; we could have gone on in to Port-au-Prince; we could have done any of a dozen things on a mere whim or chance.

I never did get the answer out of Margo, but one of the young men I had befriended in our compound later looked me in the eye and remarked (in substance): "You saw things, didn't you? You don't believe it, but you could *always* see things if you wanted to. We know, and we were watching you. We have always watched you and, although you are foreigners, we feel you are good people." (All of this paraphrased from a long talk in bad French and worse Creole.)

Perhaps the end of this story should have been another story, but somehow I feel that it is part of that whole fantastic night. If two people can see the same 'non-existent' thing, how many more could? Does one have to have the very close rapport of a devoted husband and wife, or can mere cofraternity be enough? I don't know but I'd sure like to find out.

[Oh, by the way, we went back and pulled the Rolls-Royce out of the mudpatch with the most magnificent team of oxen I have ever seen.]

EPILOGUE

IN SITU

THE PROBLEM AND SIGNIFICANCE of "Things" was discussed at some length in our previous opus of that title, and I hinted therein that we greatly need an "-ology" or science of same. For this I suggested somewhat facetiously that this should, in accordance with the accepted style of modern nomenclature, be founded on the Latin word *Res* which meant simply "things": and thus, Resology. On mature consideration, and as a result of encouragement by others, we somewhat reorientated our society to this end by abbreviating its official title to S.I.T.U.[80] Most people deplore the creation of new terms and designations: we delight in them. So, willy-nilly, while being forteans we may refer to ourselves as resologists, and if anybody asks you what that means you have at least what is called a talking point. Comes then the matter of *situ*.

We dote upon dictionaries and resort to them at the drop of a pronoun. In this case, you will find that the perfectly acceptable Latin phrase, *in situ,* has been around in the Anglosaxon languages for centuries, and that it means "In its original place". What more could we ask? We, as an organization, have actually been in situ for two decades, and our society since its inception two years ago has likewise. Further, our interests lie primarily and specifically in the "original places" where Things turn up. This may all sound horribly like a sort of embryo *status quo* but believe me when I say that if any department of enquiry gets you off the pot, the pursuit of resology does. What I mean is: the damnedest *things* keep turning up, and if you are going to prosecute any *re*search upon their incidence you just have to get going and get out in the field. Which brings up the next question.

As we also remarked before, there are all manner of things, but one of these constitutes a rather special category. This is composed of *Objects*. This has a most interesting origin and hence definition. We have to go back to what is called the "Middle Latin" word *objectum,* said to be the "neuter" of *obicere* meaning "to throw in the way of" from *jacere*, meaning "to throw". The "*ob*" bit meandered into New Latin from somewhere as a prefix meaning "in the way of", "against", or "towards". We find this most revealing. An object therefore is something thrown at you with the implication that it will obstruct—here's old "*ob*" again—your path. As a result of this, we find the whole concept perfectly splendid. What is more, it brings me rather neatly to my next point, though I cannot restrain myself from observing at this conjuncture that, in the hope of being *Objec*tive, we find ourselves in a really very strange *Situation.*

We have become ensnarled in something approaching a major battle with what I can only call "the left"—meaning those as far opposed to the orthodox, or "right", as possible—on a point of policy. This is the dividing line between the material and the non-material. This is a frightfully difficult question of itself but it can be very simply resolved by equating the concept of "material" with the matter of Objects. To explain this, I ask to be permitted once again to employ the classic differentiation between Geists (Ghosts) and Poltergeists. The former are non-material in that they cannot be weighed or measured and their incidence is dependent upon somebody's sayso. (This is not to deny the reality of the things.) For instance, if somebody asserts that he or she had a long talk with his or her grandmother last night but affirmed that the lady had been dead and buried for forty years, one rather naturally asks for some confirmation of such an assertion. If none of a concrete nature is forthcoming, one has to assume that the incident was of a non-material nature.

If, on the other hand, somebody rings up and says something like: "Hi! There's something going on over here, all mom's frying pans are flying around, and my brother got ink poured down his neck and we ain't got no ink in the house", one takes an entirely different view of things. This concerns *objects* that are what we call material; and, unless one is a complete dolt, one dashes over to have a look-see. If the pans continue to take off, and more ink or anything else you can collect in a sterile tube turns up, you have got yourself something thoroughly *Objec*tive with which you can, or ought to be able to, cope. If these manifestations do not recur, or re-occur, in your presence, however, there is nothing much you can do but go home.

The statements of the fellow who called you are just as worthless as the other one who had a chat with his grandmother.

Now, as I said before, we find ourselves in a really very strange *situ*ation when we come to this matter of what is called *objectivity*. Of the reports discussed in this book, you will note that four are really purely subjective—Neo-dinosaurs, Giant Skulls, Underwater People, and the case for "mass" hallucination—in that they do not offer an *object* even as a starting point. These are included not just to display our good faith as it were, but because they seem to us to very strongly support the subjectivists, if I may so designate them. We cannot deny that somebody had a chat with his departed grandmother if we are willing to listen to and spend time speculating upon reports that others have seen living dinosaurs in the Congo, giant skulls in the Aleutians, or people walking about underwater in West Africa. And, we personally most certainly cannot do so if we have the audacity to publish our own "experiences" in Haiti. And this brings me to still another point which I wish very earnestly to make.

I believe in the incidence of what is called hallucination simply because I dream, and I have been given to understand that everybody else does. Dreams are presumably hallucinatory; at least we must assume so until it is proved that they are some sort of free television beamed at us from some outside source. But "mass hallucination" I do not accept as of now, and despite the account that I give in Chapter 13. That a couple as closely linked mentally and physically as my wife and I could "see" the same things at the same time but which were manifestly not there is one thing; that whole hordes of people *not* intimately connected or even connected at all should see the same things precisely is either pure rubbish or definite proof that they are under external control and are made to see them by outside forces. And for the love of Pete (whoever he was) don't bring up psychology; it would be the last exercise capable of explaining such a concept as "mass hallucination". Which, in turn, brings us to this most dreary of all matters.

Nobody has defined psychology and it is not a science. Manipulating human thought may well now be an art, but you most assuredly don't need what is today called a psychologist to implement this. Juju-men and dictators do a much better and cleaner-cut job—and on both individuals and on masses. On the other hand there is a perfectly good science called Ethology which covers all the maunderings of the so-called psychologists and a great deal besides, and which has also already gone far toward explaining the behaviour of living entities. Studies included in this expertise cover all aspects of the behaviour of living things in *natural* conditions, which is to say in their natural environment. (Similar studies of living things in unnatural conditions, such as zoos, laboratories, domestication, and other forms of confinement are now classed under Behaviourism.) Confusion arises when we come to those living entities which we call human beings.

For some, actually quite illogical but nonetheless excusable, reasons we developed the notion that Man has been living in an *unnatural* environment since some ill-defined point when he gave up collecting and hunting and became a sedentary agriculturist. What has been overlooked is that the new environment that man then started to create for himself and which has ended up in our present-day technological consumer-civilization is merely a natural process of natural evolution and is therefore just as natural as the uncultivated world of prehistory. Thus, our behavior is a matter of ethological study (not behavioral) unless of course we are studying the behavior of persons in confinement or other restraint. And the performance of the mind—as opposed to the brain on the one hand and the personality of the individual on the other—is just as natural as that of the material body. Matters like Industrial Psychology are just as ethological as is medicine; and "things" like dreams and hallucinations are likewise. To explain the latter we should turn to the chemists rather than to aesthetes who profess to analyze and influence human thought. There's nothing psychological about the effects of hallucinatory drugs any more than there is about dreams resultant from eating a surfeit of pork chops before going to sleep.

There must be an explanation of why my wife and I thought we saw the same nonexistent things at the same time in Haiti. This *could,* I must presume, be that said identical vision was imposed upon us by some outside forces. On the other hand, it *could* be due to some form of mental link between us and possibly one activated, processed, and implemented by our physical computer boxes that we call our brains. Let it not be forgotten, however, that during what we call "sex" there is an interchange of chemicals in fluid form, and with such fluids go all the DNAs and other complex organizational patterns, so that two people of opposite sex can, by cohabitation, become truly interwoven in a most real and material sense.

If anybody can suggest a third alternative I would be most happy to hear of it but I must warn that I will not accept any explanation of what might be called a religious nature. If you want to try and convince me that God or some other Supreme Power, or some mere god imposed this seeming reality upon us: *Don't*. As for the concept of the universal mind, as propounded by such as Carl Jung, I do not think I need even speak—there are just too many "unexplaineds" in it even for us. This case may at first appear quite illogical, and it is, from the point of view of our current logic; but then, logic is wholly dependent upon our present understanding of reality. If we found out (and could prove) that an interchange of body fluids included chemical trigger substances for mental procedure, at least one form of telepathy would become acceptable and open for study.

The other three cases included in the preceding chapters which are based wholly and solely on reports are in no way as complicated and are much easier to accept. They are straightforward accounts of Things which *could*, logically, be obtained; at least in the case of fresh bones of neodinosaurs or of giant human skulls. The people who allegedly "walk for water" would have to be filmed and timed, and those doing this would in turn have to be filmed so filming and timing. Better still would be to invite a family from West Africa to visit one of the larger scientific institutions and demonstrate their abilities. In the meantime, however, I presume to submit to you these cases since they each have a number of sort of corollary strings attached. Not even the giant skulls are wholly illogical and especially if one allows for all manner of exaggerations and misinterpretations and other muddles—notably that more than one *thing* may be involved.

The rest of these accounts are pinned to some object or objects that you can, as the saying goes, "get your teeth into"; and these are the kind of things that we spend our time investigating in S.I.T.U. and, as far as possible and whenever possible *in situ*. And at this point I feel that

I should reiterate what I laid down in my last book ("Things", Pyramid Pubs., Inc., 1967) regarding our objectives in the Society.

We are a group, a few hundred strong, for the most part of people who had scientific training and who are today employed either professionally as scientists or have moved into other fields. Many others are in the communication fields as writers, editors, or publishers, or in the radio, television, and film industries, and especially in their technological departments. There are also among us many technologists and most notably engineers; a high proportion of service personnel; and for the rest, just plain interested citizens. We were founded some three years ago, as of the time of writing, at the suggestion, and then the insistance of some fifty founding-members who wished to pool their accumulated resources. The primary objective was to preserve their material, get it organized, catalogued, filed, and made available for use. To do this, we had to tackle one of the greatest problems of our current age—Classification.

Knowledge is accumulating by geometrical progression. Its classification has exercised men's minds since the dawn of history. Today it is of special concern and it falls into the bailiwick of what is called "Library Science"—which is to say the Data-Collection expertise. The computers have come to the aid of our previously most laborious and rather "primitive" cataloguing methods. All these old methods have "broken-down" under the strain of the flood of new knowledge but, at the same time, the computers have elaborated the basic taxonomic structure to such a point of complexity that nobody, other than a specialist, can understand it. Therefore, we have gone back to a simplification of the whole business, covering all fields of knowledge. This, we have found, is best expressed as follows:

   I. MATHEMATICS: The Structure and Behaviour of Mensuration. Number, Quantity, Probability, Arithmetic, Algebra, Geometry, Trigonometry, Calculus, Topology, the Theory of Games, and such related matters of calculation.

  II. COSMOLOGY: The Structure and Behaviour of Existence. Ontology, Metaphysics (classical), Space, Time, Locus, and such items as Coincidence.

 III. CHEMIPHYSICS: The Structure and Behaviour of

Matter. Nucleonics, Chemistry, Physics (classical) Electrics, Electromagnetics, Magnetics, Mechanics, and related technologies, as Engineering, etc.

IV. ASTRONOMY: The Structure and Behaviour of Gross Bodies. The Universe(s), Galactics, Stellar and Solar Astronomy, Planetology, Selenology, Meteoritics, Astrophysics, etc.

V. GEOLOGY: The Structure and Behaviour of the Earth. This includes everything connected with the Earth Sciences—Atmosphere, Hydrosphere, and Lithosphere—plus the sublithic core. Thus: meteorology, hydrology, glaciology, oceanology, geophysics and geomorphology, geology (classical), volcanology, seismology, petrology, mineralogy, etc. Also—geography, geodesy, mapping, dating, etc.

VI. BIOLOGY: The Structure and Behaviour of Animate Entities. These are the Life-Sciences (apart from mental expressions) but including Exobiology as well as the life indigenous to this planet. It thus covers *all* life-forms, from the possibly non-material to man; and embraces Protogeanology, Botany, and Zoology; Histology, Physiology, and Anatomy, and Human Physical Anthropology (i.e. man, physically, as an animal).

VII. ANTHROPOLOGY: The Structure and Behaviour of Human Enterprise. Archaeology, Pre-history, History, Ethnology, Sociology, Folklore (but not Mythology), Philology, Economics and the Arts, Architecture, Agronomy, and other useful arts, and their related technologies.

VIII. MENTALOGY: The Structure and Behaviour of Intellect. Logic, Ethics, Aesthetics, Mythology and Religion; Psychology, Mysticism, and the Occult; Comparative Intelligence, etc.

Given this simplified framework, there is nothing that lacks a place. For practical purposes and use in our work, the key words are, of course, "Structure and Behaviour", and it is of first importance to ask oneself just what particular aspect of any item is of concern (to us) at the time. Thus, for example, in considering a "fall" of an unknown species of fish from a clear sky, is it the type of fish (zoological), the weather (geological), or the *method of arrival* of the fish (chemiphysical) that is of first concern?

Obviously, it is the last, since the weather is, in this case, purely negative, while the identification of the fish (specifically) is a purely secondary zoological matter. The *event* is the important aspect of the record; and this is a physical matter—i.e., it is concerned with the behaviour of matter.

This way of handling things is of course a masterful simplification but it is not an oversimplification. And when it comes to "Things" it turns out to be just about the only way in which they can be classified. But there comes then another and much greater problem.

While things and individual facts become ever more patternized and thus classifiable, knowledge as a whole is becoming ever more muddled and, at the same time, ever more specialized. The more facts we accumulate and the better insight we gain of reality, the more they link up, so that it is becoming increasingly difficult to decide just where to lodge any particular item. We mentioned the matter of a fall of live fish from a clear sky and decided that it was the "falling" that was of primary interest. But what then to do with a clear, simple, and well-reported case of a large hairy ultra-primitive hominid, allegedly observed for some hours by more than two people, that causes some form of jamming of the observers' senses, and also considerable mental confusion and disorientation? The main item is still the creature—an ABSM as we call it —but brain control, let alone direct physical disruption, is quite another matter. Almost everybody immediately plumps for so-called "psychology" in such an instance. However, we do not. We feel that, as explained in Chapter 12, it is a purely physical matter that falls within the purlieus of electromagnetic or other "wave" studies. It's pretty sure now that such brain "control" and mind "patrol" problems as hypnotism and much of SSP are *not* definable on the electromagnetic spectrum, but nevertheless, there is considerable evidence that they fall squarely in the department of chemiphysics and have nothing to do with the purely mental—even if such a thing as "psychology" exists *per se,* and apart from a purely physical basis.[81]

Here, however, we have two "unexplaineds" in one. There are other cases wherein three or more matters of interest to forteans, and thus to S.I.T.U., are combined, and the more information we gather on any as yet unexplained items the more links and crossovers we encounter; just as do those who are investigating the "explaineds".

This should not be allowed to faze us as everything is manifestly linked to everything else in the first place, but at the present stage of our understanding we have to erect a set of pigeon-holes and try to fit everything into one or another lest we go under in a welter of complexity. After all, one can always take anything out of one hole and slip it into another just as postal-clerks do with the incoming and outgoing mail. Besides, one can add pigeonholes by multiplication or by subdivision, though we strongly urge that the latter rather than the former procedure be adopted for, if we keep multiplying, we will end up once again with the appalling overcomplication recently created by the computers, which is the very thing (there's *that* word again) we want to avoid.

If there is any one thing that the dipoles of religion and science do agree upon, it is the essential unity of the whole, which is to say that everything in the world, the universe, the cosmos, and simple "existence" itself is ultimately inter- and intra-linked. And this goes for the non-material, including "thoughts", just as much as it does for photons, atoms, molecules, and all gross forms of matter, both inanimate and animate. This was the thought of the Gautama Buddha, and the teaching of the Essene named Christos by the Greeks. It is the ultimate finding of the nuclear physicists and the cosmologists. Yet, there is no reason why we should not try to classify what we learn about the various and probably endless aspects of The Whole. I don't think even a Judaeo-Christian can object to this since one of their age-old admonitions is "Know thy God".

This has gotten rather "deep" and it might be regarded as not just unexpected but in some ways inexcusable, coming from us. Nonetheless, it cannot be denied; and, further, the longer you dip into what we call mysteries and the deeper you dig into them, the more often you come bang smack up against the matter of universality. And this constrains us to state flatly that it is the failure to appreciate this that is at the root of the present failure of our educational system. In fact, I repeat, "Science is the Pursuit of the Unknown"; and, I will add: so is Religion.

Ivan T. Sanderson
The Society for the Investigation of the Unexplained.
Columbia, N.J.

BIBLIOGRAPHY

1. Sanderson, Ivan T., "There Could Be Dinosaurs", *The Saturday Evening Post*, 3 January 1948.
2. Owen, Richard, "Report on British Fossil Reptiles, Part II." Report of the British Association for the Advancement of Science, Eleventh Meeting, Plymouth, July 1841, pp. 60-204.
3. Colbert, Edwin H., *Dinosaurs: Their Discovery and Their World*, New York: E. P. Dutton, 1961; *Men and Dinosaurs*, New York: E. P. Dutton, 1968.
4. Bartholomew, John, *Advanced Atlas of Modern Geography*, New York: McGraw-Hill, 1962.
5. Gobler, F., [letter to editor], *Cape Argus*, July, 1932; also as F. Grobler, *Rhodesia Herald*, 15 July 1932.
6. Maydon, Maj. H. C., quoted in Lane, Frank W., *Nature Parade*, Sheridan House, 1954.
7. Hagenbeck, Carl, *Beasts and Men*, London, 1909.
8. Ley, Willy, *The Lungfish, The Dodo, and the Unicorn*, New York: The Viking Press, 1948.
9. Heuvelmans, Bernard, *On the Track of Unknown Animals*, London: Rupert Hart-Davis, 1958.
10. See demographic maps published by American Geographical Society.
11. Sanderson, Ivan T., *Caribbean Treasure*, New York: The Viking Press, 1939.
12. Sanderson, Ivan T., *Animal Treasure*, New York: The Viking Press, 1937.
13. Lepage, quoted by Lane, Frank W., "Mystery Animals of Jungle and Forest", *National Review* (London), July 1937.
14. Von Stein zu Lausnitz, Freiherr, quoted in Ley, Willy, *op. cit.*
15. Stephens, Sergeant, quoted by Millais, J. G., *Far Away Up the Nile*, London, 1924.
16. James, C. E., [letter to the editor], London *Daily Mail*, 26 Dec. 1919.
17. Koldewey, Prof. R., *Das Ischtar-Tor in Babylon*, Leipzig, 1918.

184 • *Bibliography*

18. Bakker, Robert T., *Discovery*, June 1968 [see also New York *Times*, 2 June 1968].
19. Heuvelmans, Bernard, *In the Wake of the Sea-Serpents*, New York: Hill & Wang, 1968.
20. van der Horst, C. T., private communication, 10 November 1948.
21. Lilius, Aleko, "Strange Footprints in African Sands", MSS.
22. Lilius, Aleko, "I Saw the Monster of Umfolozi Lake", *True* Magazine, July 1944.
23. Currie, H. H., private communication, 21 November 1950.
24. Colbert, Edwin H., *Men and Dinosaurs*, New York: E. P. Dutton, 1968.
25. Tampa *Sun Tribune*, 14 November 1948; and others.
26. Sanderson, Ivan T., "The Tracks", *True*, June 1951.
27. St. Petersburg *Times*, 26 July 1948; Clearwater *Sun*, 26 July 1948.
28. Private communication.
29. *Palaeondyptes antarcticus* from the Eocene of New Zealand.
30. Scott, Hugh, "The Stormy Threshold of the Antarctic: Origin of the Subantarctic Islands", *American Scientist*, October 1950; and Jeannel, Dr. Rene, "Au Seuil de l'Antarctique: Croisière du 'Bougainville' aux Iles des Manchots et des Eléphants de Mer," Pub. no. 5, Editions du Muséum National d'Histoire Naturelle, Paris; also Mémoires du Museum National d'Histoire Naturelle, October 1940, vol. 14.
31. Romer, Alfred S., *Vertebrate Palaeontology*, 2nd edit., Chicago: University of Chicago Press, 1945.
32. Burton, Maurice, "Unseen for fifty years and now rediscovered in New Zealand", *Illustrated London News*, 11 December 1948; "The Takahe Reappears: First Photographs of the Live Notornis", *Illustrated London News*, 1 January 1949.
33. Duff, Dr. Roger, *Moas and Moa-Hunters*, Wellington, N.Z.: Government Printer, 1957.
34. "Eggs of Takahe in the Home of the Flightless Notornis", *Illustrated London News*, 27 May 1950.
35. Richdale, L. E., "Notornis is Found", *Nature Magazine*, March 1951.
36. Sanderson, Ivan T., "First Photos of 'Bigfoot', California's Legendary 'Abominable Snowman'", *Argosy*

Magazine, February 1968; "More Evidence that Bigfoot Exists", *Argosy* Magazine, April 1968.

37. Sanderson, Ivan T., "The Ultimate Hunt", *Sports Afield*, April 1961.
38. Dinsdale, Tim, *The Leviathans*, London: Routledge & Kegan Paul Ltd., 1966; *Loch Ness Monster*, London: Routledge & Kegan Paul Ltd., 1961.
39. Sanderson, Ivan T. *Abominable Snowmen: Legend Come to Life*, Philadelphia: Chilton Company, 1961; paperback edition, New York: Pyramid Publications, 1968.
40. Hardy, Prof. Alister, quoted in AP verbatim report of March 6, 1960 conference of marine scientists, Brighton, England, in New York *Herald Tribune*, 7 March 1960.
41. Koenigswald, G. H. R. von, *Meeting Prehistoric Man*, New York: Harper & Bros., 1956.
42. "A Giant Ape of 500,000 Years Ago: New Light on the Monster Gigantopithecus of Prehistoric China", *Illustrated London News*, 13 April 1957.
43. Heuvelmans, Bernard, *Dans le Sillage des Monstres Marin*, Paris: Plon, 1958.
44. Private communication.
45. Sanderson, Ivan T., "Riddle of the Frozen Giants", *The Saturday Evening Post*, 16 January 1960.
46. Digby, G. B., *The Mammoth and Mammoth-Hunting in Northeast Siberia*, London: H. F. & G. Witherby, 1926.
47. Pfizenmayer, E. W., *Siberian Man and Mammoth*, London: Blackie & Son Ltd.
48. Hapgood, Charles, *Earth's Shifting Crust*, New York, 1958.
49. *Quick Frozen Foods Magazine* (see cumulative index); and Tressler, D. K., *The Freezing Preparation of Foods*, New York, 1943.
50. Hibben, Frank C., "Evidence of Early Man in Alaska", *American Antiquity*, vol. VIII; and other papers.
51. *Ibid.*
52. Sanderson, Ivan T., "The Spreading Mystery of the Bermuda Triangle", *Argosy* Magazine, August 1968.
53. Gaddis, Vincent, "The Deadly Bermuda Triangle", *Argosy* Magazine, February 1964.
54. Gaddis, Vincent, *Invisible Horizons—True Mysteries of the Sea*, Philadelphia: Chilton Company, 1965.

55. Carstoiu, John, "The Two Gravitational Fields and Gravitational Waves Propagation", *Proceedings of the National Science Foundation*, in press.

56. Zaitsev, Vyacheslav, "Visitors from Outer Space", *Sputnik*, no. 1, January 1967.

57. Hapgood, Charles H., *Maps of the Ancient Sea Kings*, Philadelphia: Chilton Company, 1966.

58. *The New Yorker*, 30 November 1968.

59. Riesenfeld, Alphonse, "Ignorance of Physiological Paternity in Melanesia", *Journal of American Folklore*, 1945, pp. 152-53.

60. Orton, Arthur W., "The Four-Faced Visitors of Ezekiel", *Analog*, March 1961 (reprinted in Earley, George W., *Encounters with Aliens*, Los Angeles: Sherbourne Press, 1968.).

61. New York *World Telegram and Sun*, 10 August 1961.

62. Lugli, Prof. G., private communication, 10 November 1961.

63. White, John T., *A Complete Latin-English Dictionary for the Use of Junior Students*, Longmans, Green, and Company.

64. Sanderson, Ivan T., *"Things"*, New York: Pyramid Publications, 1968.

65. See *Journal of the Royal Geographical Society of London*, England—Cumulative Index for numerous papers.

66. American Society of Dowsers, Inc., *Quarterly Journal*, Fall 1968.

67. Matacia, Louis J., *Dowsing Introduced to the United States Armed Forces*, privately printed, 1968.

68. "Mechanical Dowsing", *Pursuit* (S.I.T.U. Journal), vol. I, no. 4.

69. Kennedy, Prof. George C., private communication, 2 December 1968.

70. Sanderson, Ivan T., "The Animals Have It on Us", *The Saturday Evening Post*, 24 October 1953.

71. Tannehill, Ivan Ray, *Hurricanes*, Princeton: Princeton University Press, 1943.

72. "What Science Knows About Dolphin 'Talk' ", *Science Digest*, May 1965; Burton, Maurice, "Dolphins Are So Touchy", *Illustrated London News*, 20 February 1965.

73. Keynes, R. D., "The Generation of Electricity by Fishes", *Endeavour*, October 1956; Burton, Maurice,

"A Fish Using Radio-Location?", *Illustrated London News*, 28 April 1951.

74. Sanderson, Ivan T., "The Mystery of Migration", *The Saturday Evening Post*, 15 July 1944.

75. Frische, Karl von, *Experientia*, 2, 397-404, 1946; *Die Naturwiss*, 35, 1948; *Experientia*, 5, 142-48, 1949, 6, 210, 1950.

76. Waterman, T. H., Science, *111*, 252, 1950.

77. Hocking, B., and Mitchell, B. L., "Owl Vision", *Ibis*, *103a*, 284-88, 1961.

78. Ingram, Collingwood, "The Phenomenon of Sporadic Hibernation in Nestling Swifts", *Illustrated London News*, 16 September 1950.

79. Sanderson, Ivan T., "Haitian Hallucination—The City That Wasn't There", *Fate* Magazine, October 1965.

80. *Pursuit* (S.I.T.U. Journal), vol. I, no. 4.

81. Note: There is now a vast literature on this but it constitutes a subject quite separate from the matters discussed in this book.

INDEX